THE STORY OF

Good Queen Bess

Then the Bishop placed the crown upon her head

GREAT EVENTS IN THE LIFE OF GOOD QUEEN BESS

5 *llows Sir Walter Raleigh to send xplorers and colonists to America, 1584*

6 *Sends Sir Francis Drake on an expedition around the world, 1586*

7 *Sees the Spanish Armada defeated by the English fleet, 1588*

8 *Allows Mary, Queen of Scots, to be beheaded for conspiracy, 1587*

THE STORY OF

Good Queen Bess

By ALIDA SIMS MALKUS

Illustrated by DOUGLAS GORSLINE

ENID LAMONTE MEADOWCROFT
Supervising Editor

PUBLISHERS Grosset & Dunlap NEW YORK

COPYRIGHT, 1953, BY ALIDA SIMS MALKUS
The Story of Good Queen Bess

PRINTED IN THE UNITED STATES OF AMERICA

Library of Congress Catalog Card No. 52-13747

To

Elizabeth Tudor

In memory of one of the
greatest queens of history

Contents

CONTENTS

Illustrations

THE STORY OF

Good Queen Bess

She smiled at them all, and thanked them prettily

CHAPTER ONE

The Little Princess

HER Grace is in a temper," sighed good Dame Bryan. The gentle lady peeped through the curtains at the Princess Elizabeth Tudor.

The little girl stood before the diamond-paned windows of the dark old library. She gazed stormily down into the lovely English garden below.

"She is lonely without a playmate," whispered Dame Bryan to herself. "Poor mite! Not a soul to visit her in months! Not even a glimpse of her little brother Edward."

Dame Bryan coughed gently to let her royal charge know that she was there. But pride kept the little Princess from turning around, even though she heard her governess. She would let no one see her weep.

"I am the daughter of the King of England," she thought crossly. "Yet here I am, penned up at Hunsdon—with no companions. I am nearly ten years old, and I am treated like a prisoner." She clenched her fists.

"I may not even ride abroad alone," her unhappy thoughts ran. "No one wants me. My father—" And now the tears were streaming down her cheeks.

"Now, now, Your Grace," Dame Bryan coaxed behind her. "Master Grindell says your Latin is done for the day. Let us take a walk in the garden—"

"Walk in the garden!" screamed the Princess, whirling around. This was too much! "Walk in the garden, forsooth!" She looked wildly about for something to throw or to break.

"Am I a bumblebee, or a mole, perchance, to *walk* in a *garden!*" she stormed.

Her eyes were red from crying. She was a slender little girl, with satin-smooth hair of a pale golden red. Her skin was white and fine.

The Princess Elizabeth stood stiffly, unhappily, but at that moment a cheerful voice rang out from the hall.

"Oh-ho, there! I have news for Your Grace." It was Master Grindell, Elizabeth's tutor. His pleasant face appeared at the door. He came forward smiling.

A letter was in his hand. "Come now, a smile in exchange for this," he teased.

"Oh, Grindell, Grindell, what is it?" Elizabeth brushed away the tears, and held out her hand imperiously. Her tutor bowed, and handed her the letter. It was sealed with the King's seal.

The Princess Elizabeth unfolded the heavy white paper. As she read the letter her chin lifted. A smile broke over her fair face. Her small rosy mouth trembled. Then her eyes flashed with delight.

"His Majesty has sent for me! Do you hear, dear Dame Bryan? Do you hear, Grindell?" she cried. "My father has sent for me! I am to go to Whitehall to Court."

The news spread down the halls like fire. His Majesty, King Henry the Eighth, had sent for Her Grace, the Princess Elizabeth! In but a few moments the hostler was telling the gardener . . . "She's not lived there at Whitehall since she was three, poor lamb. In 1536,

had tossed his little son up into the air, just as once he had tossed her. And he had looked at her no more. But it was not her father's throne, only his love, that she wanted.

"Come, come, Your Grace," Dame Bryan broke into Elizabeth's dreams. "You have almost nothing fit to wear. Stand up, pray, while I measure you. La, la, Your Grace has outgrown everything!"

"Then I shall have all new clothes," cried Elizabeth, dancing about the room.

The sewing woman came bustling in, and the village draper was sent for. Elizabeth managed to stand still while she was measured, and the draper spread his best silks and woolens on the bed. The Princess looked at these materials and frowned.

"But this cloth, it is ugly!" she cried. "I will not wear this at Court. I want something bright and golden!"

Everything was thrown into confusion. The draper was sent back to his shop for a piece of russet velvet. He had hardly returned when in came Grindell with a big packet. It had just come, by a special messenger on a fast horse.

"From the Queen, for the Princess Elizabeth," Grindell said, bowing. "With the compliments of Her Majesty, Queen Catherine."

The package was opened. There were silks, velvets, sprigged taffeta, embroidered satin, and muslin as sheer as cobwebs. Elizabeth was delighted.

"Darling Dame, forgive my tantrum," she cried, in radiant good humor once more. "And you, good sir, the draper. I shall wear your russet velvet too. It will become my hair, will it not?"

She smiled at them all, and thanked them prettily, and they forgave her, for the sweet way she had.

"Ah, she can be the best behaved of any child ever I knew," sighed Dame Bryan to Master Grindell. "And clever. She was only six when she sewed a shirt for her little brother; with her own little hands."

"She is a good pupil," agreed Master Grindell. "But I think studies are over for today. Her Grace is too excited to practice her penmanship. She may ride, instead."

Soon Elizabeth stood upon the mounting block, in her shabby little habit and old hunting hat, with its bronze plume. She set her foot in the groom's hand, and sprang light as a feather into the saddle.

Then she was away like a hound after a hare, and her riding master had to press his horse to keep up.

"Softly, softly, Your Grace," he called as he drew alongside. "Not so fast, Your Grace. Gather the reins up firmly as you take yonder hedge. Lift your mount."

Over the hedge like a bird she flew. Laughing and triumphant, she galloped on.

"Splendid, Your Grace," cried the riding master. "A good seat, a light hand on the rein. I think that His Majesty will be pleased when he sees what a fine horsewoman he has."

Elizabeth smiled gratefully. Then she was off again, jumping two ditches without rising from her saddle. Flushed and happy, she pulled up at Hunsdon Gate.

Grindell was waiting for her. "Your Grace looks lovely," he smiled. "The ride has brought color to the cheeks, and new sparkle to the eyes."

"Tell me, dear Grindell," she said softly, as he lifted her down from the saddle, "do you think that His Majesty will like me again? Will he still be disappointed in me because I was not born a boy?"

"He will find pleasure in you, Your Grace, I do believe," replied the tutor, as they walked toward the Manor House. "You have learned much since you began your studies. But there is one thing, Your Grace—" Master Grindell paused as they entered the great hall.

"And pray, what is that, my master?" asked Elizabeth a bit pertly.

"It is that Your Grace might well remember always what I have taught you," Grindell warned. "You are too quick to speak what is in your mind. You must not let Your Grace's tongue run away with you."

"Oh, I shall remember, Master Grindell, I shall! I promise!" Elizabeth replied earnestly.

That night as she made ready for bed, she looked with distaste at her shrunken, mended nightshirt.

" 'Tis the last time I shall wear this shabby rail," she laughed.

"Come now, Your Grace, try to get to sleep." Dame Bryan had closed and fastened the windows, and pulled the curtains close against the night air. Now she came to draw the bed curtains close also. Her royal charge must not take cold from the night mists.

The Princess Elizabeth snuggled down in her great poster bed, and drew the feather quilt up about her chin. She thought of her father. Sometimes it must be hard for him to be a king, and lonely, too. Perhaps that was why he had married so often.

His first wife had been a Spanish princess. She was the mother of Elizabeth's half sister, Mary. Then the King had married a beautiful girl named Anne Boleyn, who was Elizabeth's mother. Next he had married Lady Jane Seymour, the mother of Elizabeth's little half brother, Edward. Now she was dead, like the others, and lovely Catherine Parr was the Queen.

"I shall see the Queen soon," Elizabeth thought with a little smile. "And my father, too."

Suddenly she felt uneasy. She had heard that her father had a terrible temper. When people disobeyed or offended him, he often had them cruelly punished. Sometimes they were even beheaded.

"But I shall behave most properly," Elizabeth told herself, "and take great care not to displease him."

She sighed happily. She could hardly wait to set out for the splendid Court of her father, King Henry the Eighth.

CHAPTER TWO

Elizabeth Goes to Court

"MAKE way, make way, make way for Her Grace, the Princess Elizabeth," cried the equerries, as the royal coach lurched through the little towns and hamlets along the way to Whitehall.

The Princess sat beside Dame Bryan, and Master Grindell sat opposite. The side seats of the coach were crammed with trunks and bundles.

Elizabeth looked out at the fair countryside, at the little stone cottages with thatched roofs. The villagers cheered and waved as the coach passed by. They had lined up along the road to see the daughter of their King. But the royal coach clattered on, with two coachmen up in front, two footmen up behind.

"Let us stop and talk with some of the people, dear Master Grindell, do," Elizabeth begged.

But no, it was a long drive down to London, twenty miles at least. So on they lurched through mud puddles and holes.

A fair was going on in the next village, and bear-baiting. The merrymakers crowded around the coach and would have stopped it. But the drivers lashed out with their whips and the coach rolled on. Two beggers clung to the sides and the footmen pushed them down, stepping on their dirty, clawing hands.

Shouts and shrieks followed the coach now, and ugly words. Dame Bryan put her hands over Elizabeth's ears. What were they saying? That she was a witch's child, no proper heir to the King? Was that what they said?

Elizabeth clenched her teeth and her fists. "I *am* a proper heir," she said fiercely. "I'll show them some day."

Grindell leaned forward and spoke earnestly. "Your Grace must never say such a thing," he said. "You must never speak of your right to the throne. Nobles have lost their heads for less than this. Edward is the heir now. And Mary—"

"Shall my sister Mary be at Court?" Elizabeth asked quickly.

"No, Your Grace," replied Dame Bryan. "She will stay at Newhall, with her guardians. It is a sign of great favor that you are sent for. I think that the invitation must have come from your stepmother, Her Highness, Queen Catherine."

Elizabeth was well pleased that Mary would not be there. The dark Spanish eyes and the sullen face of her half sister made Elizabeth uncomfortable.

"Mary does not like me," she thought. "And I do not like her very much."

These unhappy thoughts were forgotten the next moment, for as the coach clattered past a village green they saw a wedding party dancing.

As the coach drew up, the bride and groom came forward bowing and curtsying. The bride tossed her lovely bouquet into the carriage and it fell into Princess Elizabeth's lap.

"Oh, I would love to stop and dance with them!" exclaimed Elizabeth eagerly.

"Huzza, huzza!" the wedding guests cried. "Three cheers for the Princess Elizabeth!"

But the coach rolled on. It was not for a princess to dance upon a village green, said Dame Bryan.

And now it was long past dark, and Elizabeth had been asleep for some time. The coach jolted more slowly over the ruts and cobblestones and came to a stop. They were in London! They were at Whitehall itself!

Every window of the palace was alight. The

music of harp and spinet floated out upon the night air. How beautiful, how exciting! The Princess Elizabeth, stiff and weary, was suddenly wide awake.

They led her up wide stairs, along stone-flagged galleries, and at last into a high-ceiled room, with heavy beams overhead. She gazed at the walls which were hung with rich old tapestries. How splendid her father's house was! Hunsdon had been a simple country manor, with no such beautifully carved furniture.

"The Princess's apartment is right next to the Queen's," said the footman. He lit all the candles and then withdrew.

Elizabeth wondered how soon she would see the King and Queen. But she told herself she must not seem childish, nor ask too many questions. She would wait.

"Come, Your Grace," Dame Bryan spoke affectionately. "Let us wash off the dust of travel and change Your Grace's garments."

Elizabeth first chose the gown made of russet velvet, for it did seem pretty with her shining hair. "But no," she decided, "I shall wear the sprigged taffeta which the Queen sent me;

I think that she will be looking to see it."

The taffeta was a lovely dress too, with a tight bodice and full flowing skirts, and sleeves laced with velvet cords.

She was dressed none too soon. Master Grindell appeared at the door of the room.

"The Queen presents her compliments, and requests the pleasure of Her Grace's company," he announced.

Now, now, she would see the Queen!

"My throat is quaking like that of a frightened frog," she thought. "Come, Elizabeth, hold up your chin. You may not be an heir to the throne, but you are a king's daughter."

A few moments later she stood in the doorway of the Queen's apartment. A sweet-looking woman with corn-colored hair sat across the room, smiling at her.

And then the Princess Elizabeth was curtsying deeply at Queen Catherine's feet. The next instant the Queen's arms were around her, and she was being warmly kissed.

"So this is our little Princess! And what a lovely dress! Sit by me and tell me of your journey." The Queen motioned to a hassock by her side.

Elizabeth looked up at her stepmother. The Queen had kissed her, and put her arms around her! Elizabeth's eyes grew dark and shining.

Presently the Queen rose and took Elizabeth by the hand. "We shall attend His Majesty." She smiled encouragingly, as if she knew that Elizabeth was both afraid and eager to meet her father.

His Majesty, King Henry the Eighth, was seated at the far end of a great drawing room. About him stood the lords and ladies of the Court. What a dazzling sight! Never had Elizabeth seen such beautiful ladies and so many elegant noblemen.

Their costumes glittered with jewels. Silks and velvets, brocades and laces, of sky blue, apple green, puce and scarlet, were trimmed with ermine, mink, or weasel. There was much laughter and gaiety.

The ladies swept curtsies, and the lords bowed low as the Queen led Elizabeth up to her father. Now the little Princess was standing before him.

"So, this is our young Bess!" The King's voice boomed out.

Elizabeth looked up—could this be he, her

royal father? Bluff King Hal. His wide red face beamed down at her. His small, shrewd eyes seemed to see right through her. He was fat, enormous, in his wide-shouldered, fur-trimmed robe of purple velvet. The full, puffed sleeves, which were slashed and lined with scarlet satin, and the massive gold chain hung across his vast chest, made him seem even more huge.

Elizabeth kissed his jeweled hand. He smiled, and suddenly she knew why his subjects loved him.

The King rose and towered over her. Pinching her cheek playfully, he raised her to her feet. "Come, come, my little redhead, can you play the flute and harp, as well as write letters in Latin?"

"I win from my elders at chess, Your Majesty," she said, "but do ill at playing the harpsichord or hiding my feelings." Somehow she knew that he would like a straightforward answer, and no shy head-hanging. She looked up straight into her father's eyes.

The King roared out like a bullock, and she did not know whether he was angry or pleased. Then he slapped his thigh in delight. "My own child!" he cried. "Honest and fearless!"

The King rose and towered above her

By this time, the center of the room had been cleared. Out rushed two dwarfs. They were dressed magnificently, the little man exactly like the King, the tiny woman in a gown just like that of the Queen. No one had expected this, so there was much laughter.

As the dwarfs waddled elegantly down the room, the King's Fool, William Somers, appeared. The stripes on his clothes were sky blue and poppy-colored, and bells tinkled from his cap and stick. On his shoulder rode a little monkey dressed like a bishop.

The Fool led the little man and woman up to the chair where the King had sat, and set them both within it.

"The King's Fool will dare anything," whispered the ladies. "He is a favorite here at Court."

Now William Somers had left the dwarfs. He stooped to whisper in a lady's ear. She was overcome with laughter. Now he swooped down and put his lips to the ear of the Princess Elizabeth.

"If I dared set *you* on the throne," he whispered, for her ear alone, "I would. But Father Time himself will do that."

Aloud he cried to the King, "I did but peep

into Her Grace's head, and thought I had looked into His Majesty's own head. Your Grace's pardon!"

Everyone held his breath. Would the King be angered? But no, he let out his mighty laugh again. "So, even the Fool sees that the child takes after her father!" he exclaimed.

All the lords and ladies laughed merrily and nodded wisely. So, His Majesty looked with favor on his young daughter.

All kinds of tricks and jests followed. There were songs and verses too. Most of them Elizabeth did not understand. She was thinking of what the Fool, William Somers, had said. Did he really mean—that Father Time would put her on the throne?

The little dwarfs came hurrying up to her. They put their arms around her and hugged her. "Send for us tomorrow," they cried, "to play with you. We are Rarities!"

The Princess Elizabeth fell asleep that night in a great beautiful bed hung with rose velvet curtains. Her dreams were of Rarities and jesters, and dancing on the green. But somehow, something dark followed her, frighteningly.

With morning light she wondered what was true and what was dreams. When Dame Bryan pulled aside the bed curtains for her, she hurried to the window. Opening it, she looked out to see what lay beyond the Royal Palace of Whitehall.

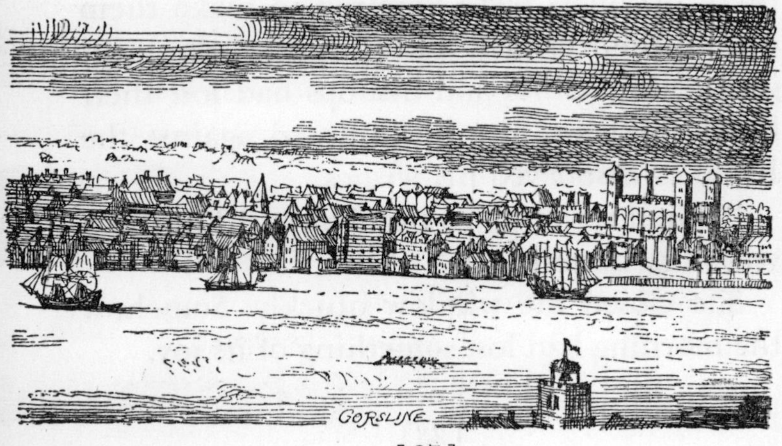

The roofs of London stretched away on either side of the river Thames with spires and gables, towers and turreted walls. A great gray castle rose from the riverbank on the outskirts of London.

"What is it?" Elizabeth asked.

"Ah, that is the Tower, Your Grace, my pet." Dame Bryan shuddered as though a cold wind had blown over her.

The Tower! What child of England had not heard about the Tower? There were royal apartments in the Tower where important visitors to England might stay. And yet it was a mighty prison and fortress, too.

Many tears had been shed there. Many cries of pain had echoed from those cold stones. For there prisoners were tortured to make them confess their crimes. There, behind the great gray walls, nobles and bishops had lost their heads, because they had plotted against the King, or disobeyed his wishes.

"I shall never go to the Tower," Elizabeth vowed to herself.

She closed the window quickly. Somehow the morning had lost something of its joy.

CHAPTER THREE

A Princess in Disgrace

THE Royal Palace of Whitehall was a busy place. The King had matters of state to attend to. The Princess Elizabeth scarcely saw her father or the Queen for the next few days.

The Rarities came to play with her every afternoon. Elizabeth beat them at chess, now and then, and they were very cross about it. But she always gave each one some candied chestnuts and a clever toy, and they went off all smiles.

One night Elizabeth supped with her father and the Queen. Afterwards the lords and ladies gathered again in the great hall. There was talk of trouble with Scotland and with other countries. The King was in a very bad mood.

He spoke loudly and laughed much. But there was a sting to his words. It seemed to Elizabeth that the counselors and gentlemen of the Court always tried to agree with her father.

"They are afraid of him," she thought. "But I am not, though I must guard my tongue."

This was hard to do, however. The talk was bright and sparkling. Many questions were asked. Although she was so young, she could usually think of answers to them. She was glad that Grindell had always *made* her *think*.

Tonight they were to have charades. Elizabeth was wearing her handsomest dress, a moss-green satin, trimmed with darker velvet and light brown fur. The gentlemen, especially Admiral Tom Seymour, said that the young men would soon be coming from far and near to marry her.

Suddenly the King's voice rose in argument above the harpist's music. "Even a child could understand that," he was shouting. "Here, young Bess, what would you say if We said that We planned to send ships against Ireland, France, and Spain, and troops to Scotland?"

"Your Majesty's Grace," the words came before she could stop them, "England has no navy and only a few ships. So I would say 'No' in four different languages."

A ripple of laughter arose. But the King's eyes flashed. It was *not* the right answer! A hush fell over the company.

"You have a pert and forward tongue in your head, lass," he said coldly. He waved her away.

Elizabeth felt a sudden terror in her throat. Her eyes misted with the rebuke. She wanted to throw herself at her father's feet, to kiss his hand, to win a word of affection and forgiveness.

But the Queen had motioned a lady in waiting to lead the Princess away. And Dame Bryan came to take her to her apartment.

Elizabeth lay stiffly in her great bed. Her throat was dry, and her eyes were dry. But her heart thumped against her chest. She was frightened and wretchedly unhappy.

So this was the end of everything. She had made a mistake straightaway. "Oh, my hasty tongue!" she thought. But what was it? What had she said that was wrong? She did not know and neither did Dame Bryan.

Long after the palace was quiet Elizabeth heard a gentle step. The curtains of her bed parted, a soft hand stroked her brow. Queen Catherine's voice spoke gently. "Tomorrow is another day, my sweet." She stooped to kiss the young Princess Elizabeth good night.

Now the tears came, and fell upon her silken pillow. And so young Bess cried herself to sleep. Yes, another day came; but another sharp disappointment came with it.

"The King commands that Your Grace keep to your rooms," said Dame Bryan, sniffling. She could not see why her charge should be punished just for being clever.

Elizabeth felt the disgrace keenly. Also, she had missed the charades and now she would not be able to see the wonderful play that was to be given tonight.

Master Grindell came and they sat in the window seat together. He told her stories of courage and patience. And then he reminded her of how in her grandfather's time there had been a frightful war in England. The War of the Roses.

"It very near ruined the land," he said. "And worse, it killed off most of the young nobles. Have you forgot, Your Grace, what started it?"

"There was no heir to the throne," answered the Princess promptly, "so every noble wanted to seize it for himself."

"There was no *son* to be the heir," corrected Grindell, "so the two chief families and their followers fought to the death to try to seat one of their sons on the throne."

"They had better have let a woman rule than to fight like that," said Elizabeth.

Grindell nodded. "There has never been a woman ruler in England," he said gravely. "It has *always* been the eldest son who has inherited the throne. And you know what happened soon after Edward was born. Your father had Parliament pass a law that neither you nor Mary should ever rule the country. But if—" Grindell stopped thoughtfully.

"If what?" Elizabeth wanted an answer.

"If the King should change that law and if anything should happen to Edward, then Mary would inherit the throne. And then, after her, Your Grace, you are next in line. So, some day you *might* be the Queen of England."

Dame Bryan brought in the tea and cakes just then. When she had left Grindell spoke again. "But remember, Your Grace must never mention your right to the throne. If you do, you will be suspected of every plot against the throne. Plotting is treason. And the punishment for treason is—death."

"I shall never speak of it, dear Grindell," whispered the little girl. "I shall never forget."

At supper time, Elizabeth had a delightful surprise. A tiny little woman came riding into the room upon a great mastiff. Elizabeth had never seen so dainty a creature. She was no dwarf, but, rather, like a fairy.

"I am Lady FitzHerbert, Your Grace," she piped in a tiny, fairylike voice.

They supped together by candlelight. Then Grindell came back, smiling.

"Your Grace," he said, "the Queen has bidden me to fetch the Princess Elizabeth onto the covered balcony, from which she may see the play. Without being seen," he added.

"But—but if the King my father learned

that I had left my room," Elizabeth thought, "he would be very angry at me, and perhaps at the Queen. What shall I do?"

Aloud she said, "The Queen is most kind and dearly thoughtful, Master Grindell. Thank Her Majesty from my heart. But I have a strange feeling in my stomach, Master Grindell. I fear I may be ill. I think—I think I must retire."

And indeed, she did feel ill suddenly and went straightway to bed.

Months passed, and the young Princess was allowed to go where she pleased about Whitehall. Yet the King her father paid no heed to her.

But one fair spring morning Elizabeth was told that she was to ride outside London with the royal hunting party. Her heart was filled with pride and pleasure as she cantered along in that handsome company. A gentleman in waiting was at her side, a groom was close at heel.

The King rode ahead, galloping back among the company every now and again.

"My father is a superb horseman," thought Elizabeth.

"His Majesty outrides everyone," said the young courtier who rode beside her, "and he is the best huntsman, too."

"His eye never seems to rest upon *me*," thought Elizabeth wistfully.

At a wide field in the country the riders pulled up. There was to be a show of horsemanship. Two young nobles failed at the jump of a hedge and a ditch beyond. But it was nothing difficult, Elizabeth thought. At Hunsdon she took such jumps daily.

When her turn came the grooms motioned

her back. But already, light as a feather on the sleek mare's back, she had urged her horse forward. In a moment she was sailing like a bird over hedge and ditch.

She came cantering back across the field, flushed and happy. The King himself was watching!

"Well done, lass," he cried out. "Come near. A good seat, a firm light hand. Mine own daughter! May you ride so through life!"

She had pleased His Majesty! After that day Elizabeth was once more allowed to go to the nightly gatherings. But alas, there came a night when her quick tongue again got the better of her, in spite of her good resolutions. The King's eyes flashed. He was very angry.

"By St. Hubert!" he cried. "This is too much! Take the child from my sight!"

The faithful Grindell appeared quickly and whisked her away from the royal presence. But he could not save her from the royal wrath this time. The King commanded that young Bess should be banished from Court.

CHAPTER FOUR

Elizabeth in Exile

"WHAT is going to happen to me? Where am I to be sent?" The Princess Elizabeth's lips quivered as she looked at Master Grindell.

Sadly Grindell told her that she was to be sent to Hatfield, the royal estate twenty miles west of London. There she would be with her little brother Edward, and they would share the same tutors.

"His Royal Highness, the Prince of Wales, is now seven, you know," Grindell reminded her, "the age at which the education of royal children begins."

"And will you come with me, dear Grindell?" asked Elizabeth anxiously.

"That I shall, Your Grace," replied Grindell heartily. "And my friend Sir Roger Ascham is coming too, to teach you French and poetry. He is the greatest scholar in England."

"And Dame Bryan?" Elizabeth hardly dared to ask. "Is she to come, also?"

Master Grindell looked away unhappily. "The Queen Her Majesty has arranged for the Lady Ashley to be Your Grace's governess now," he said.

Elizabeth's eyes filled with tears. It was bad enough to be banished from Court. But it was worse to be separated from Dame Bryan, who had taken care of her as long as she could remember. Suddenly she began to weep stormily. Dame Bryan wept too, when a royal coach clattered away from Whitehall on a warm sunny morning in mid-July. Inside the coach was the Princess Elizabeth, on her way to Hatfield—and exile.

Several months later a boy and girl sat bent over their books at a long table in the Hatfield library. Sunlight streamed through the high, leaded windows. It shone brightly on a red head and on one as yellow as gold.

"Has Your Grace finished the Greek translation?" asked Master Grindell of the red head.

"Long since, master," replied Elizabeth. "I am now translating a French book which is to be a present for Her Majesty, my stepmother."

"I know my Latin verbs, Sir Roger," the small boy spoke up importantly. "But please give me a new history lesson. I am tired of the old."

While Sir Roger heard Edward recite his verbs, William Grindell looked over the story which Princess Elizabeth was translating.

"I shall bind the book myself, too, Master Grindell," Elizabeth said eagerly. "See, I am already embroidering the cover. Lady Ashley is helping me; but I am doing all the work myself."

She showed him a canvas cover, beautifully embroidered with purple and yellow pansies, and with gold and silver braid.

"Oh, do you think the Queen will like it?" she asked wistfully.

"She will be delighted with it," Grindell told her.

Edward came bounding over and seized his sister's hand. "May we have our game of badminton now in the garden?" he cried eagerly. "Hurrah, hurrah, come along, sister," and he pulled Elizabeth outdoors.

Those were pleasant days at Hatfield. When Elizabeth and Edward were not busy at their studies the hours were filled with music, dancing lessons, riding, and games.

Then into the joyful life of the two royal children came a dark shadow. On a late summer's day a royal coach drove up through the gates of Hatfield. Out stepped a young woman and her attendants.

"The Princess Mary!" gasped Lady Ashley, as she leaned from the window.

The Princess Mary came up the grand staircase and into the great hall. The children and their tutors welcomed her warmly; but she met them coldly. The King had ordered her to visit her younger sister and brother, she said.

Mary was now twenty-eight years old. She would have been pretty, thought Elizabeth, but that her skin was sallow, and her mouth tight and turned down at the corners. She always seemed cross and unhappy.

It was an unpleasant visit. By the end of the month Elizabeth's feelings were ready to burst. One day in the study they did. Mary was tormenting her.

"You and I, Edward," said Mary, "are of more noble blood than Elizabeth." Mary looked coldly at her half sister. "Her mother's father was but a common tradesman."

Elizabeth stood up, clenching her teeth and her fists. She would not quarrel! She would not make a scene! She would not pay any attention to Mary. But just let her say another word!

Mary did. "And her mother was common also," she went on cruelly.

Elizabeth could bear no more. A storm of anger swept over her. Red waves of light blinded her eyes.

"It is not true," she cried. "It is a lie, a lie!" Quick as lightning, she seized the inkpot and threw it at the Princess Mary—her royal sister, her elder!

The Princess Elizabeth was sent to her room immediately. Later she apologized for throwing the inkpot. But she and Mary were no more friendly than before.

And then a most fortunate thing happened. Sir Roger Ascham called all the household together in the great hall. There he read aloud an important piece of news.

" 'His Majesty, King Henry the Eighth, has asked Parliament to pass a law which will allow his daughters to be heirs again to the throne of England,' " he read. Then he added, "This means that if anything should happen to Edward after he has become the King, Mary will rule the country. And if anything should happen to Mary, Elizabeth will be the Queen."

"Hurrah!" cried little Edward.

He ran over to his sister Elizabeth and threw his arms around her. Then, with a true courtliness, he turned to his sister Mary and kissed her hand. Mary stood as one bewitched. And after that she was more pleasant to everyone.

As for Elizabeth, the news brought her a feeling of comfort. Now she knew that her father did not hate her after all. And her right to the throne had been recognized.

Both Elizabeth and Edward were glad when their sister Mary left. "Come, Edward, I will beat you at battledore," cried Elizabeth after studies every day.

"Your arms are longer," Edward would complain, but he would always seize his shuttlecock, and often win from Elizabeth.

Days passed into weeks, weeks into months. No word came from Whitehall, for the King had gone off to France to the wars. The out-

side world did not touch the children. Here at Hatfield were gardens to play in, lanes and fields to ride in, wonderful stories to listen to of an evening.

William Grindell and Roger Ascham took turns reading aloud tales of ancient heroes and stories of England's past.

Many of those stories were about English kings. Always, it seemed to Elizabeth, there had been fighting over who should rule the

Soon Edward's ninth birthday was at hand

country. Men had plotted to get the throne, often killing those who stood in their way.

"It seems hard to have had so much of killings," said Lady Ashley one evening, "but I think all who plot against a rightful heir should surely be punished."

Elizabeth turned from the fire. "Do you truly believe that, good Lady Ashley?" she asked. She had come to love her governess, and to respect her judgment.

"I do indeed, Your Grace." Lady Ashley rose and drew Edward to his feet. "If a king did not punish treason by death, he would not long be king. He would be murdered by the traitors. Come now, sweet Edward. Your Highness must to bed. Already the owl hoots in the chimney."

"These happy days cannot last," Elizabeth said when Lady Ashley returned to the library. "Something will happen any minute now. I know it."

"Hush, hush, Your Grace, say not so," Dame Ashley chided.

Soon Edward's ninth birthday was at hand. Elizabeth planned all kinds of surprises. She wrote a poem for him. She embroidered a cap of velvet. She and Lady Ashley planned a charade.

The day came and there was a feast in the long hall. The great candelabras were filled with twenty candles each. On the table were stuffed pheasant, broiled brook trout, roasted chestnuts, lambs' tongues with capers, plums in honey, and little sweet cakes.

Edward had never been happier, nor had Elizabeth. But when the feast was ended, Master Grindell gave them bad news.

"Now that Edward is nine," he said, "the King thinks he must be with boys of his own age. Tomorrow he is to go to Hertford to live with his uncle, the Duke of Somerset."

So the happy life at Hatfield was ended. The children were separated. Roger Ascham took little Prince Edward to Hertford. William Grindell and Lady Ashley were commanded to go with Princess Elizabeth to the royal palace at Enfield.

CHAPTER FIVE

The Boy King

IT WAS very lonely at Enfield without Edward. Elizabeth looked every day for a messenger bringing a letter from her brother. She had already written to him. At last the letter came.

"Sweetest Sister," wrote Edward. "Change of place did not vex me so much in fact, dearest sister, as your going from me."

Ah, he did love her then! One person whom she could claim loved her truly. And here Christmas was upon them, and she must pass it without him!

Yet Christmas at Enfield was a pretty sight. The villagers sang carols beneath the windows, and the servants dragged a great Yule log into the main hall. There was a mummer's play, and more carols were sung, and at last a great boar's head, with an apple in its mouth, was fetched in, steaming.

Everyone received gifts, and then sat down to the table and feasted. Fingers served for forks, and though the Princess Elizabeth often wiped her face most daintily with her napkin, most of the company wore greasy smiles from ear to ear.

And then the day was past and gone. The

New Year of 1547 came in. But the Christmas garlands still hung on the walls when a royal coach stopped before the door of Enfield. And there was Edward!

"My uncle sent me word from Court to come here," he told Elizabeth. "And he will soon be here himself. I do not know why."

Edward's uncle, the Duke of Somerset, was in favor at Court. Had something of importance happened there? What was he going to tell them?

When the Duke arrived, Elizabeth stood awaiting him, holding tightly to Edward's hand. Grindell and Lady Ashley stood beside them. The Duke faced them, tall, lean, serious.

"I bring news of great importance." He paused a moment and then said in a loud, ringing voice, "The King is dead!"

The words echoed down the halls, and back from the heavy raftered ceilings. "The King is dead!"

What? Was Henry Tudor, King Henry the Eighth, dead? Bluff King Hal, her father, gone?

Tears came into Elizabeth's eyes. Her arms

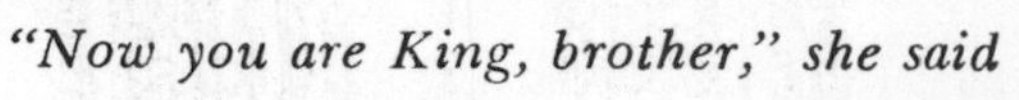

"Now you are King, brother," she said

went around her brother. She lifted his hand then, and pressed her lips upon it.

"Now you are King, brother," she said.

Grindell and Lady Ashley came and bowed to the young Edward. His uncle fell on one knee before the boy.

"Long live the King!" shouted the Duke. And now the cry rose through all the Manor of Enfield. "Long live the King!"

Young Edward turned uncertainly to his sister and threw his arms around her. "Stay with me, sister," he murmured. Now that he was King, he was frightened.

"If I could stay, I would, Your Grace, my sweet," Elizabeth whispered. "But they will not want you to have girls for companions, I fear. You must be a man."

Edward stood very straight. He threw back his shoulders, and his eyes gazed ahead, as though he were looking into the future.

His uncle laid a hand upon the boy's head. "I shall be a father to Your Majesty," he said.

Edward looked at him gratefully; but there were tears in his eyes. The next morning the royal children were taken down to Whitehall. There a magnificent funeral was held.

Queen Catherine told them that their father had been ill for some time. Indeed, he had died three days before the news was given out.

"Why was this? Why did not the Duke of Somerset let the news be told at once?" Elizabeth asked Lady Ashley that evening. She stood in her room in the palace, looking over the roofs of London just as she had four years before.

"Edward is so young that the Council of nobles will have to appoint a guardian to rule in his place," replied Lady Ashley. "There may be jealousy and fighting over this. Of course Somerset will want to be Edward's guardian. No doubt he held back the news, hoping to be appointed quickly. But the Council has not yet agreed to this. And the matter has not been settled."

"Poor little Edward," said Elizabeth. She seemed to have grown older overnight. "He is tired out with the excitement and the journey. He is not strong, Dame Ashley, you know. I am glad Sir Roger put him straight to bed."

Darkness had come suddenly, and now a cold rain was falling. London was very dismal.

There was a knock on the door and Sir Roger Ascham entered. He looked worried.

"The Duke has got Edward out of his warm bed," he said in a low voice. "They have ridden off to a meeting of the Council. I told the Duke that the boy was tired. But he would not listen to me." Sir Roger was upset and angry.

"But it is raining!" cried Elizabeth furiously. "The Duke is thinking only of himself. He wants the nobles to see how much Edward likes him, and how bright Edward is. I know! And Edward is worn out with our long ride yesterday, and the funeral and everything."

Fire seemed to smolder in Elizabeth's eyes, and gleam in her red hair.

"Shh, child," warned Lady Ashley sharply. "Speak softly. We do not know who may be listening at keyholes. Somerset may rule in the Palace tomorrow if he has his way tonight; and he will not like to be criticized."

Sir Roger nodded. He, too, was worried.

The next day Edward and the Duke returned. The Council had agreed that Somerset should be Edward's guardian. But the little King had caught a bad cold and was suffering from loss of sleep.

Sir Roger insisted that he must go right to bed, and Elizabeth stayed by his side. She put hot cloths to his feet and gave him hot herb drinks. The royal physician wanted to bleed him when his fever rose at night. But this no one would agree to. Edward recovered slowly and Elizabeth stayed with him most of the time until he was well enough to be up again.

Almost three months passed. Then Elizabeth was told that she must go to live with her stepmother, Catherine Parr, at Chelsea.

"Dame Ashley," she said as her clothes were being packed, "I hate to leave His Majesty. He is far from strong. Cares and studies should not be put upon him at this time. Do you think any harm will come to him?"

"No," replied Dame Ashley. "I do not think anyone would plot against His Majesty."

The next morning Edward sent for Elizabeth. "Sister," he said, "when I am old enough I shall take good care of you. And I am going to give you Hatfield, I promise you, and whatever place you want. My uncle seems to think it best for you to live at Chelsea. But do write me, sister. And I shall write you—about everything."

CHAPTER SIX

A Queen for Nine Days

IT WAS a fair spring morning in the year 1553. The Princess Elizabeth stood in a window looking out over the green lawns of Ashridge. Edward had given her this lovely royal estate four years ago.

Six years had passed since Henry the Eighth had died. For six years Edward had been King. The Duke of Somerset who had been his guardian was dead, and another uncle named Northumberland had taken his place.

"I do not like Northumberland any better than I liked Somerset," thought Elizabeth. "He is a scheming man who wants only what is good for himself and not what is good for England or for my brother. Edward obeys him sometimes without thinking. Perhaps if Edward were stronger—"

She sighed. Her brother had never been very well. Twice she had received word that he was dying. Elizabeth shuddered.

"If Edward should die," she said to herself, "my sister Mary will become the Queen. She can be very cruel—and I think she hates me."

Elizabeth was nineteen now. She was a handsome young woman and her red hair was like a fiery halo around her white face. As she stood at the window, fingering the heavy gold necklace which she wore with her plain green gown, William Grindell stepped through the door.

"She is a queenly person," he thought. He hated to give her the message which had just come.

"Your Grace," he said when Elizabeth turned from the window, "I have news for you. Edward has named your cousin, Lady Jane Grey, as his heir to the throne."

"But he cannot!" Elizabeth exclaimed. "It was my father's wish that Mary and I should be heirs to the throne after Edward. And Parliament passed a law confirming it."

"Even so, Edward has made a will naming Lady Jane Grey," Grindell said sadly. "Northumberland persuaded him to do it. Lady Jane is married, you know, to Northumberland's young son. If she reigns, then Northumberland will still be the most powerful man in the country."

Through the open window at this moment came the sound of a horse galloping up to the manor door.

"What now?" Elizabeth cried, clasping her hands to her heart. In a few moments a letter was brought to her.

"Grindell!" Elizabeth looked up from the letter. "Edward is very ill again, at Greenwich." Her face was filled with grief. "He will die, I fear. Northumberland has sent for me. And for Mary too."

"What shall you do?" Grindell asked in a low voice.

He did not trust Northumberland and he was afraid some harm might come to her from Northumberland's men.

"I shall leave immediately." Elizabeth seized a cloak. "Please order my coach at once. I must see my brother before he dies."

"Well then, God grant that Your Grace ar-

rives in time," said Grindell earnestly, and hurried to order the coach.

In a very few minutes the coach and four horses rolled up to the carriage entrance. The household of the Princess Elizabeth was in a state of great excitement.

"God save Your Grace, God save Your Grace!" the cry rose as the Princess entered her coach. All the people of her household and of the countryside loved Elizabeth.

Down the long drive, over the rough country roads, the coach bumped and swayed. Inside Elizabeth sat, holding to the straps. Her thoughts raced ahead of the horses.

Would she get to Greenwich in time? Dear Edward. He thought he was doing the best for England . . . If Lady Jane really were made Queen, what would happen to Mary and to herself? Northumberland might seize them both and have them killed.

But what about the people of England? Would they allow Mary and herself to be put aside? Edward really had no right to will the crown away. Would the people not rise and defend the daughters of King Henry the Eighth?

"It is in God's hands!" Elizabeth thought.

Late that afternoon two royal coaches were nearing Greenwich by two different roads, jolting wildly over the ruts.

"Hurry, hurry," cried Elizabeth to the driver. "Oh, let them make speed," she prayed.

The Princess Elizabeth sat very straight, but her eyes were bright with tears. In the other coach rode the Royal Princess Mary, now a stern-looking woman of thirty-six.

The coaches met at a crossroads. A messenger waited there. Elizabeth recognized him at once. She leaned from the coach.

"Ascham!" she cried. "Have you news? How is my brother?"

"King Edward is dead!" Roger Ascham bowed his head to hide his grief. "Yes, it is really so."

"Too late, too late!" sobbed Elizabeth. "Come back to Ashridge with me, dear Roger."

"You are not going on to Greenwich?" asked Ascham in surprise.

"No. See, Mary is already turning back herself. Northumberland would find it too easy to seize us both, and kill us or throw us in prison. Besides, I feel too ill to go on."

Elizabeth was indeed ill. As soon as she reached home she was put to bed. There, four days later, she received news from London. A messenger came racing up the road, his horse glistening with sweat and lather.

"The Lady Jane Grey has been proclaimed Queen!" he cried.

"England will not have her!" declared Roger Ascham. "I see sad days ahead."

Sad days indeed! It was only a week later that the word came: "England is rising. The people will not set aside Henry's daughter, Mary Tudor."

And presently came another message: "The Princess Mary's defenders have seized the Duke of Northumberland. They have sent the Lady Jane and her young husband to the Tower. Mary is now the Queen."

"Poor little Lady Jane," said the gentle Roger Ascham to Elizabeth. "A queen for only nine days. From the throne to the Tower. What next?"

"What next?" Elizabeth sat up in bed. "I must set out at once to greet my sister, the Queen. Leave me, pray, while I dress."

A thousand countryfolk followed Elizabeth's coach as she drove toward London. Mary Tudor had already reached the city.

When Elizabeth met the new Queen she knelt before her and said most earnestly, "Accept the devotion and loyalty, Your Majesty, of Your sister Elizabeth."

But Mary looked at her coldly and made no reply.

CHAPTER SEVEN

Through the Traitor's Gate

IT WAS soon plain to be seen that the Princess Elizabeth was to be shown no favors at Queen Mary's Court. The Queen dismissed Lady Ashley, whom Elizabeth loved dearly, and named a Lady Tyrwhit to take her place.

"I believe that Lady Tyrwhit has been put here to spy on me," Elizabeth told Roger Ascham one fall evening, several weeks later. "I am uneasy, good Ascham."

"So are the people of England," Roger Ascham replied. "They thought it right when the Queen had Northumberland beheaded because he wished Lady Jane Grey to be the Queen. But they are angry now because Mary insists that she is going to marry King Philip of Spain, even though Parliament has passed a law against it. The people do not want a foreign king in this country. I fear that there will be trouble unless Queen Mary changes her mind."

Ascham did not know that, even as he spoke, trouble was already brewing. Though the night was dark, a horseman was riding away from London. He turned cautiously toward the country home of one Sir Thomas Wyatt, of Kent. When at length he arrived there, he found a group of men waiting within the dimly lighted hall.

"Welcome, my Lord of Suffolk," they greeted him.

All through the night the men talked in low voices. The Duke of Suffolk, who was the father of the little Lady Jane Grey, listened earnestly.

"Our plot is well laid," said Sir Thomas Wyatt at last. "Everything is now settled. You, Suffolk, will rouse the people of the Midlands. I will gather together the men of Kent. On the morning of February the twelfth we will join forces outside of London."

"I shall be there," promised Suffolk. "My daughter is still in the Tower. I shall not rest until I have freed her, and swept Mary from the throne."

"And I shall not rest until we have placed Elizabeth upon it," replied Sir Thomas Wyatt.

"Does the Princess Elizabeth know of this?" asked Suffolk. "Is she with us?"

"She has been told nothing," said Wyatt. "But I think she will not refuse when we place her on the throne."

The plotters soon returned to their homes. Weeks passed. Then, on the morning of February twelfth, people living in Whitehall Palace heard men fighting in the street. Elizabeth opened her window to see what was happening.

"Thomas Wyatt is at Hyde Park corner," cried Roger Ascham at her shoulder. "He has a large company of men. They are fighting the Queen's guards. It looks as if they are trying to attack the palace."

"What can this mean, good Sir Roger?" The Princess Elizabeth clutched her throat with both hands, as though she could already feel the axe there.

"It can only mean that they wish to seize the Queen," replied Ascham in a low voice.

"God save us, Ascham," exclaimed Elizabeth in horror. "My sister will blame me! She will think that I plotted this."

They could do nothing but watch. But the fighting did not last long. Wyatt and his men were no match for the Queen's guards. Many of the men were killed. Others ran away. Wyatt himself was taken prisoner, and carried off to the Tower.

A few hours later the Tower guns boomed out and the bells began to toll. What had happened? Ascham went to find out. He returned quickly.

"They have all gone to the block!" he cried. "The Lady Jane, Suffolk, her father, and her young husband have all lost their heads."

"Poor lovely child, to lose her head at seventeen!" exclaimed Elizabeth.

Hardly an hour later they heard that Wyatt had accused the Princess Elizabeth of taking part in the plot. He thought to save himself by blaming her. But it did not save him. And before he was beheaded he confessed.

"The Princess Elizabeth knew nothing of this, and had no part in the plot," he cried when they came to lead him to the scaffold.

But when Mary learned that Wyatt and his men had planned to set Elizabeth upon the throne she was furious. She was suspicious of her sister and more disagreeable to her than before. At last Elizabeth asked permission to return to Ashridge.

"It is but three days' journey away, Your Grace, and I can live quietly there and await Your Majesty's pleasure," she said.

"Very well," replied the Queen coldly. "You may go."

So the Princess started off for Ashridge, to hide from the Queen's displeasure.

"What can I do now, good Sir Roger?" asked Elizabeth unhappily, as their coach jolted along the muddy roads. "The Queen will always suspect me of plotting against her, even though Wyatt did confess his lie."

"Live quietly," replied her tutor gently. "Stay away from the Court, and even from countryfolk. Spend little. Have no feasts or pageants. Study with me."

"Good Roger, I am so ill that I feel I shall die." Elizabeth lay back in her coach. Would they never reach Ashridge?

She was ill indeed, with a raging fever.

When she reached home at last, they put her to bed.

"Pray God it be not the sweating sickness," said the physician. "In one week eight hundred people died of this in London Town."

Weeks passed, and Elizabeth still lay in bed with a lingering fever. And then there came an order from the Queen commanding her to return to Court.

"Saint's mercy!" said Ascham. "Let the messenger take word to the Queen that Her Grace is ill."

But it made no difference. Elizabeth was ordered to set out at once for the Court. The Queen had sent a litter drawn by twenty-seven Spanish mules to fetch the Princess Elizabeth to London. Although she could not stand, she was taken from her bed and laid upon the litter.

Three noblemen rode ahead of her and there were two hundred and fifty horsemen to escort Her Grace. The Lady Tyrwhit rode smugly along beside the litter.

"The Queen still believes Elizabeth had a part in Wyatt's plot," thought Ascham. But what could *he* do? Nothing, but follow along.

It was a long journey. At last they reached Whitehall, but the Princess no longer felt the jolts and bumps of the journey; she had fainted from exhaustion.

"Her Grace is to remain here," said the captain of the guards, bowing, "until she is well. For safe-keeping."

It was a week before Elizabeth began to grow stronger. Even before that time, the Queen's ministers visited her. They plagued her with questions about her part in Wyatt's plot.

"Good my lords," Elizabeth said wearily, "I had naught to do with it." She turned her face to the wall and closed her eyes.

"But Your Grace knew somewhat of what was going on?" insisted the ministers.

"Let God be my judge," the sick Princess sat up and faced her tormentors, "I knew nothing of it until already it was done!" Her eyes flashed dangerously, and for the moment they let her be.

At length the Court physician said that the Princess was better, and that the Queen wished her to be moved to Hampton Court. So up the river Thames to Hampton Court went Elizabeth and all her household. There, day after day, Elizabeth waited uneasily, wondering what her sister the Queen would do next. At last she learned that she, the Princess Elizabeth, had been charged with treason.

"Write to the Queen," Ascham begged. "Tell her once more of your loyalty. Tell her you wish to be of service to her and to England. The Queen knows well that Your Grace is the best educated woman in all England. Or in all Europe for that matter."

So Elizabeth wrote to her sister. But her letter did no good. On a rainy day, a sad, gloomy

day, a barge was moored at the gate of Hampton Court. The soldiers of the Queen had come to arrest the Princess Elizabeth.

"Where are they taking me?" the Princess asked, lifting her white hands to her red hair. But she had no need to ask. She knew. They would take her to the Tower.

She stepped into the barge. Not even Ascham was allowed to come with her. Only Lady Tyrwhit whom she distrusted was beside her.

"This is the beginning of the end," Elizabeth thought.

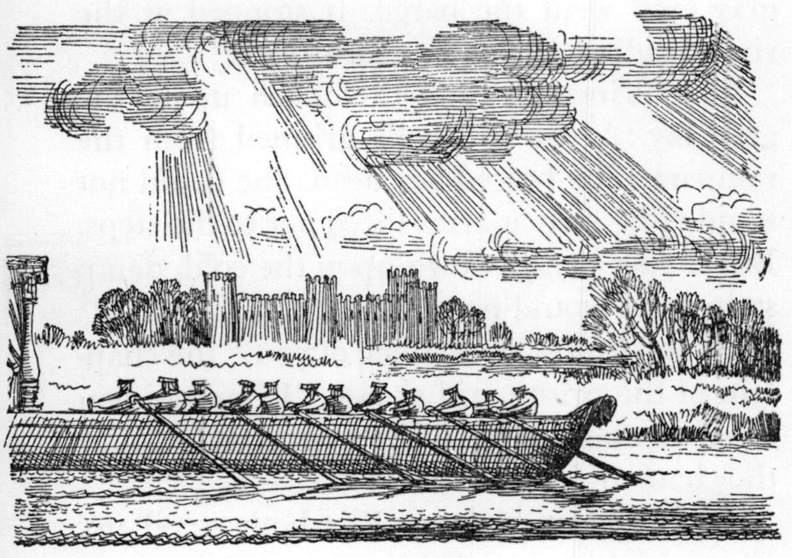

Down the gray river, nearer and nearer to the heart of London Town, the bargemen poled against the current.

"They would not even wait for the tide to go out," Elizabeth murmured, "so great was my sister's hurry."

Mary had chosen a good time, when the people of London were all indoors. Few saw the barge, and if they did they did not know that it carried the Royal Princess.

There were two gates to the Tower. One was the entrance to the royal apartments. The other was—the Traitor's Gate. Under the cold gray arch went the barge. It stopped at the river landing of the Traitor's Gate.

The Princess Elizabeth looked up at the gray sky. A row of skulls grinned from the ramparts. She bowed her head. She could not stand. The men-at-arms lifted her to the steps. But she sat herself down upon the cold, damp stones and would not enter.

"Good Your Grace, I beg of you," the chaplain of the prison said at last, "I implore you to enter and not keep the men standing, for they hate this task."

And so after an hour Elizabeth stood up.

"Here lands at these stairs," she said, "as true a subject, being prisoner, as ever landed here." She lifted her eyes, for her heart was desperate. "And before Thee, God, I speak it, having none other friends but Thee alone."

Then the Princess Elizabeth passed through the Traitor's Gate and into the dark, gloomy Tower.

CHAPTER EIGHT

From the Tower to the Throne

A LITTLE boy came running down the stone-flagged Tower halls. The patter of his feet echoed along the corridors.

"That is the fairest sound that these sad old walls have ever heard," said the Princess Elizabeth. She had stood gazing from the window toward the roofs of Whitehall. "Has there been no word from the Queen?"

"There is nothing, Your Grace." Lady Tyrwhit curtsied nervously.

Then the sound of the small footsteps stopped. There was a knock at the door. The little boy stood there. He held a bunch of primroses and marigolds in his small fist.

"Here are flowers for the Princess," he piped. He would not give them to Lady Tyrwhit. "I want to see the Princess." He pointed solemnly. "That lady with the pretty pink hair."

Elizabeth laughed outright. "What a pretty child!" she exclaimed. "What is your name?"

"My name is Giles," replied the boy. "Giles Maris. Shall I bring Your Grace some flowers every day?"

"That you shall," she said with a smile. "It will brighten this long and weary time."

The first painful suspense had passed. Now the Princess waited grimly. What was her sister the Queen going to do with her?

"While there is life, there is hope," she said aloud. "My sister has no evidence against me, Dame Tyrwhit, for there *is* no evidence."

Yet that same afternoon the Queen's agents visited her again, tormenting her with questions. "Did Your Grace not have a visit from Wyatt? Did Your Grace not agree that the rebels should seize Her Gracious Majesty, Queen Mary? Did Your Grace not consent to be placed upon the throne?"

"Does Your Grace deny this? Does Your Grace deny that?" And thus it went, week after week.

Three wretched months in the Tower passed by

Three wretched months passed by. One day Elizabeth looked down into the courtyard and saw a company of three hundred men approaching. The door opened behind her. In came Roger Ascham.

"Oh, Ascham, is this the end?" she cried. She drew him into the Bell Tower and closed the door. "What are they going to do to me?"

There came a knock at the heavy oak door. "Open, open to them, Ascham." The Princess lifted her chin proudly. But only Giles stood there. The little boy held up his flowers.

"Lady, I cannot bring you flowers any more," he said, with tears in his eyes. "They have come to take you home."

Home? Was it true? Yes, she was free. The soldiers were to escort her back to Court.

"The Queen is afraid to keep Your Grace in prison any longer," Ascham told her quickly. "She can find no evidence against you, and the people will not allow her to keep you here any longer. The people love you, Your Grace."

"Thank God for that," Elizabeth replied.

And so the Princess Elizabeth was taken back to Court. After a time the Queen said she

The little boy held up his flowers

must leave Whitehall and live in a great house at Woodstock. There she was as closely guarded as she had been in the Tower.

Meanwhile Queen Mary was preparing for her marriage with King Philip of Spain. Though the people of London tried to seem gay on her wedding day, the hearts of many Englishmen were angry, for they did not like the Spanish King.

At Christmastime Elizabeth was summoned again to Whitehall. There she knelt before the Queen and kissed her hand. The two sisters talked together for a few minutes. When she had returned to her own rooms in the palace, Elizabeth sent for Sir Roger Ascham.

"The Queen's ministers are still questioning me," she said. "How can I persuade them that I am innocent and had no part in Wyatt's plot?"

"Live quietly, Your Grace," advised Roger Ascham again. "Visit Her Majesty when she commands it. Continue with your studies. In short, Your Grace, keep on as you have been doing. Then you shall keep your head upon your shoulders and I shall keep mine."

He lowered his voice. "The people have no

love for Mary's Spanish husband," he went on. "Perhaps—"

"Careful, careful, Ascham!" Elizabeth herself had at last learned to speak carefully. "I have good news too," she went on. "I am to return to my beloved Hatfield. You, dear Sir Roger, are to go with me. And see—" The Princess held out her hands, turning a ring upon her finger. "It is from the Queen. I too gave my sister a ring in return." She smiled.

"May God be praised!" cried Ascham. "Then the Queen herself no longer distrusts you. God in His mercy and wisdom has kept Your Grace safe, through every danger and pitfall."

And so back to her childhood home went the Princess Elizabeth. She lived quietly, she studied, and every fair day she sat beneath the oaks with her books.

The years passed. One, two, three—then four went by. On a warm November day in the fall of the year 1558, the Princess sat on a bench beneath a great oak. A small girl of six was running around and around the tree. Two golden-coated spaniels raced after her.

"Round and round the mulberry tree, round and round," sang the little girl.

As the child and the spaniels stopped before her, the Princess with the red hair looked up from her book. "But it is an oak, Elspeth, my sweet," she said. She patted the golden curls of her steward's little daughter.

"I too danced around this tree as a child. And here beneath the oaks of Hatfield I am like to end my days, sitting right on this bench."

"But why shall you do that, Your Grace?" The little girl looked curiously out of her wide blue eyes. "My father says that one day you will be Queen of England and sit on the throne. And perhaps quite soon, he says. It is a bad, naughty Queen we have now."

"Hush, child!" exclaimed the Princess. "You must not say that. Someone might overhear it, and tell the Queen."

"And what would she do then?" The child's eyes widened. "Would she have me burned at the stake? Why is she cruel and bad?"

Elizabeth sighed. "It is not easy to be a queen, little Elspeth," she replied in a low voice.

Elspeth nodded gravely. Then she scampered away to play, and the Princess Elizabeth sat thinking of her sister.

Poor Mary Tudor! She had been having a difficult time ruling her people. Many of the things she had done had displeased them, and she had lost their love by marrying a foreigner.

Now her husband, King Philip of Spain, was abroad, fighting a war against France. Queen Mary was lonely without him, and often she was ill.

"My sister leads an unhappy life," Elizabeth said to herself.

She began once more to read, but after a time she looked up from her book. Sir Roger Ascham was approaching her, followed by all her household folk.

Why were they coming to her? The Princess Elizabeth looked up at the blue sky. She breathed deep of the rose-scented air of the countryside.

Something had happened. But she was ready. She had lived twenty-five years for this moment. Now it was here, whichever way it was to be—the Tower, or the Throne.

"The Queen is dead," Sir Roger said, and bowed before her.

"Long live Elizabeth, our Queen!" rose the cry from the housefolk. "Hail to Elizabeth, huzza, huzza, huzza!"

She had lived twenty-five years for this moment

"I thank my God that I have lived to see this day," Roger Ascham said. He knelt at Elizabeth's feet and kissed her white hand. "And still more wondrous," he was thinking, "that Her Grace herself has lived."

Elizabeth rose slowly from the bench. Her face was alight, her eyes shone. "This is the Lord's doing," she said. "And it is marvelous in Our eyes."

Now the news spread like magic. The villagers swarmed up the hill and gathered about the gates of Hatfield. They cheered, and wept for joy. The cruel reign of unhappy Mary Tudor was over.

From far and near the nobles hurried to the childhood home of their new Queen. The road was black with horsemen. A thousand countryfolk gathered to fetch their Queen down to London.

But Elizabeth wanted to be sure that the news was indeed true. "Roger, let a messenger be sent at once to bring me the Coronation Ring from off Mary's finger," she bade him. "Then I shall believe. For Mary would never part with it were she alive. Fetch me the ring, then, so that I may know this is no trick."

CHAPTER NINE

The Coronation

AT NIGHTFALL the next day the ring from Queen Mary's finger was laid in Elizabeth's hands. The news that her sister had died was true then, and no trick to cause her arrest. Elizabeth was indeed the Queen. And four days later she rode down to London Town. Shouts of welcome and joy rose all along the road.

"Hail to bonny Queen Bess! England for the English!"

"No more of the Spanish King Philip!"

At Charter House the Lord Mayor of London and all the City officers greeted her. The next day the new Queen rode on triumphantly, through the city and to the Tower.

But how different it was this time! Now she was taken to the royal apartments. "Now I am raised," said Elizabeth, "from being prisoner in this place, to being ruler in this land."

The coronation was to be held as soon as all preparations could be made. And on the morning of the fifteenth day of January, 1559, Elizabeth rose, and her ladies dressed her in a gown of cloth of gold. Over that was a cape of crimson velvet, trimmed with ermine. She entered her coach and drove out through the Royal Gate of the Tower. For five hundred years the Kings of England had set out from the Tower for Westminster Abbey upon their coronation day.

The streets had been cleaned and freshly strewn with gravel and sand. Sweet herbs had been scattered all along the way. The houses and shops were hung with tapestries and draperies of cloth of gold and velvet. What a beautiful sight!

The windows and the curbs were crowded with people, all dressed in their best. They had waited since before daylight to see the procession.

And here it came! First the fifers, tootle-ti-toot! Then four drummers, tarra-boom, tarra-boom! And a splendid drum major.

"Hurrah, hurrah," shouted the urchins of London Town. They capered along, turning handsprings. "Eight trumpeters, wiv silver trumpets, an' a kettledrum, blimey! an' eight more trumpets." They were wild with delight.

Now came the sheriffs on their big shining black Flemish horses. Next came the craftsmen, dressed in their liveries. Yes, the goldsmiths, the stonemasons, and on down the line —to shoe cobblers, armorers, and weavers.

Then came the Queen's lawyers, her Attorney General, Masters in Chancery, her Sergeant, all splendid in robes of scarlet velvet.

The procession was like a glorious river of flowing scarlet and gold and flying pennants. The clink of horses' hoofs, the music of fife and drum, and of children's choirs singing like angels and scattering flowers.

But where was Her Majesty, God bless her?

"Just keep watching, Moll," cried a woman in the streets. "We'll see more just looking than marching. Let the grand folk ride, and us will see the show. Here they come now!"

Yes, there were the lesser nobles, then barons, baronesses—and *now!* The coach of the Queen!

Elizabeth was magnificent! Exquisite pointed lace set off her slender face. A circlet of gold and jewels rested on her bright hair.

She bowed, she smiled, the people went wild!

As many followed the Queen's coach as had gone before it. The guns boomed out in sa-

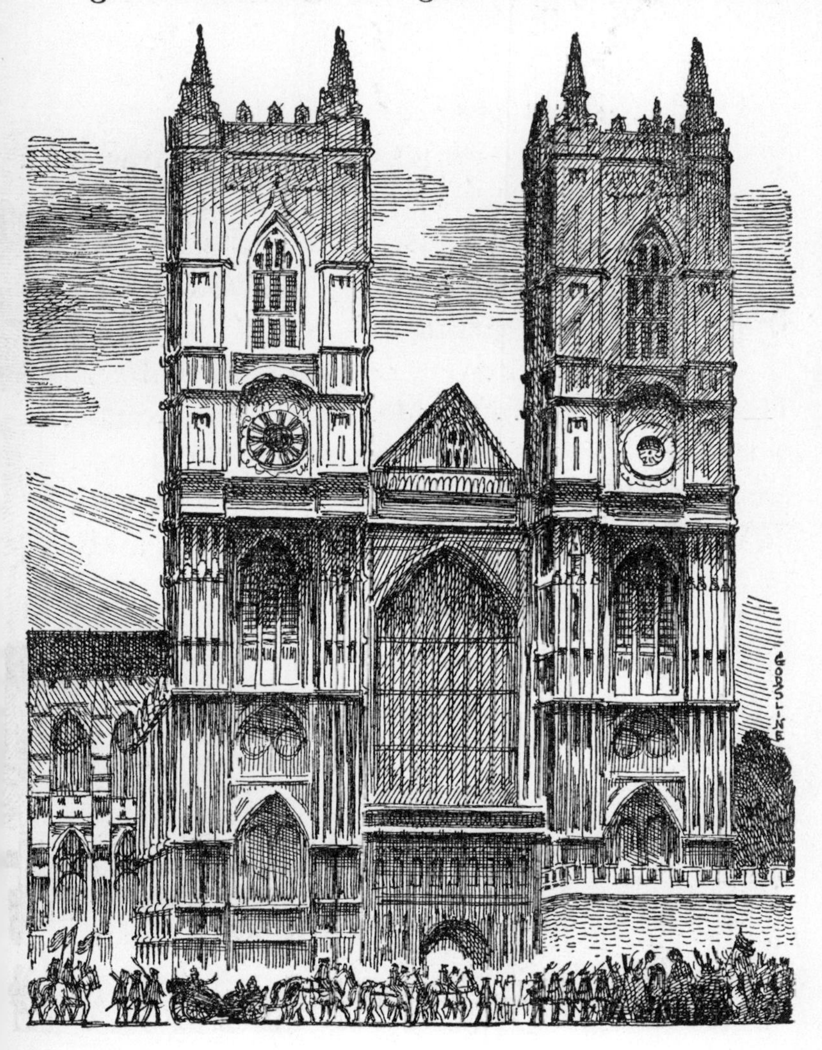

lute, and the bells of Westminster Abbey pealed. The Queen had reached Westminster Hall. The nobles were escorting her to the end of the great hall; they were seating her in the marble chair.

On the table before her were laid all the coronation treasures—the jeweled orb, the crown and staff, the scepter and the ring, the robe, the flask filled with holy oil, and the spoon. These treasures had been taken at break of day from the deep and secret chapel of the Pyx, that lies beneath the very center of the Abbey. Here they had been guarded from one coronation to another. And now the nobles presented them to the Queen.

When this was over Elizabeth rose and moved with slow and stately tread on her way to Westminster Abbey. A blue velvet carpet lay all the way from the hall to the church.

The royal robe of gold and purple brocade with silver flowers was splendid over her gold and scarlet gown. Above her head was the golden canopy borne by her nobles. Flowers were strewn beneath her feet. She was followed by a noble carrying her crown upon a satin pillow.

Elizabeth reached the church door and entered the lofty and magnificent cathedral. How sweetly the singing of the children of the choir fell upon the ear! The Queen passed up the aisle between the rows of her subjects. Could anything stop her now?

She was seated in the Coronation Chair, so old, so honored, where so many English kings have sat. Beneath its seat rested the Scottish Stone of Scone. Now she was to be anointed with the holy oil, and her ladies loosened her dress.

The good Bishop of Oglethorpe poured the blessed oil from the flask into the spoon. He anointed the Queen upon her shoulders, her neck, her brow, her hair.

And so she was anointed before God. Then the Bishop placed the Crown upon her head, and upon her finger he placed the Coronation Ring. "With this ring I am wed to England," Elizabeth vowed silently.

So the Princess Elizabeth Tudor was crowned. As she rose from the Coronation Chair the voices of her people lifted in cheers of praise and the choir sang triumphantly.

Now the time had come to celebrate and

make merry. The new Queen led the way back to Westminster Hall, while two children scattered roses before her.

One of these children was little Elspeth, who had come from Hatfield at the Queen's command. The other was Giles, the little boy of the Tower, who was now a lad of eleven.

They were seated at the Queen's feet on the platform where the banquet table was spread. Here they could see everything.

"Here comes the Queen's Champion," whispered Elspeth in Giles' ear. "See that knight in armor, who enters upon his milk-white horse?"

"Why, he is riding straight into the hall!" exclaimed Giles in delight.

The knight was shouting out his challenge to all.

"If any person deny that our Sovereign Lady be the true next heir to the Crown, here stand I, Her champion, who says that he lies and is a false traitor!"

"But none will say so," whispered Giles, "for she is indeed the true Queen. And that I for one can testify."

"And I too," said Elspeth warmly.

The knight was shouting out his challenge to all

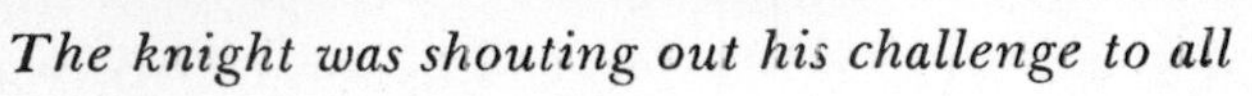

"Come, my sweet, my true champion ever," smiled the Queen, overhearing Elspeth's words. "You shall stay by me always, and be my best little maid at Court. As for Giles here," and the Queen stroked Giles' auburn curls, "he has already become a member of Our royal household."

Now the feasting began. Two great tables stretched the length of the hall. Gold and silver dishes covered the snowy cloths. Waiters hurried to and fro, bringing great platters of steaming food.

"Know you, little Elspeth," said Giles importantly, "that a hundred cooks, and as many more second cooks, have been cooking for seven days for the feast?"

He stuffed a spiced meat tart into his mouth and began to recite, "There are anchovies and coxcombs, marrow pattie and jellies, fresh-baked lampreys, beef roast and veal roast, and leg o' lamb. There are twenty crabs, sweetbreads, halibut and salmon, stuffed pigeon and pheasant, scallops, artichoke, tansie and asparagus."

Giles stopped to draw breath and stuff another tart into his bulging cheek. "And that is not all. For sweets they have eighteen mince pies, and pistachio cream, and mangoes from the Indies, and Parmesan cheese, and—well, that is but a third of it. But now let us eat, Elspeth." And he began on a leg of chicken.

"I have all new clothing," said Elspeth proudly, licking some jam from her fingers. "New gown and slip, new hose and sandals."

But it was hard for Giles to hear her, for the bagpipes playing, and the people laughing and talking filled the hall with noise.

Up in the galleries those good folk lucky enough to have seats looked down upon the feasters. Their turn would come later.

"Did you hear how loud Her Majesty swore her oath?" cried one man to his neighbor.

"Aye," the man shouted back. "The Bishop said would she make no laws unless they were for the good of the people. 'I swear,' said Her Majesty, in a good loud voice."

Now no more talk could be heard, because of the music of flutes, the barking of dogs, the cheers from many throats.

And so the people of England welcomed their new Queen.

CHAPTER TEN

To London Town

"Hark, hark, with what a pretty throat,
Poor Robin Redbreast tunes his note."

SO SANG a young lad with ruddy face and auburn curls. He sat in the bow of a barge that moved smoothly down the river Thames. It was young Giles Maris who, eight years before, had brought flowers to Elizabeth in the Tower.

"You are gay, Master Giles," said the boatman. He steered his barge out of the way of the small boats passing up and down or across the river.

"And well may I be gay," cried the boy. "I'm on my way down to Court at Her gracious Majesty's special command. 'Sing cuckoo, sing cuckoo,' " he warbled, until his changing voice cracked on a sour note.

"There's the Bear Pit, lad," called the boatman, nodding to the right bank. "And yonder are the new cock pits."

Past Strawberry Hill and Battersea they floated, and around the great bend in the river. Past Richmond Palace and Lambeth Palace, past gardens and water stairs and fair green banks.

"We're nearing London Town, lad," said the boatman, sculling his barge quickly out of the way of a large merchant ship swinging at anchor. "Never have these old eyes seen so many goodly ships upon the Thames. English ships sail everywhere today."

"Aye," said the boy happily, looking from side to side of the riverbank. "As my name is Giles Maris, old London has grown since I was a little lad in the Tower. There are more fine palaces and mansions, and fair gardens along the banks."

"When were you last here, Master Giles?" The boatman guided the barge toward the center of the stream, to ride down the current of the outgoing tide.

"Two years ago, master boatman." Giles turned to look back up the river. "A few months after Her gracious Majesty was crowned she sent me off to Eton, which is Sir Roger Ascham's grammar school. And this autumn I go upriver to old Oxford University." He leaned over the side to trail his hand in the water.

"Much has happened since our good Queen Bess came to the throne." The old boatman wagged his gray beard. "We have had peace at home and abroad."

"Right you are, Gaffer," replied Giles earnestly. "Whew, watch out, Gaffer!" A small boat had darted out from among the many ships lying at anchor and pulled alongside them. Reflected in the water Giles saw a figure rise up over the boatman.

Something struck the barge; it began to rock. The old man tumbled flat, losing his oar in the stream. Quickly Giles reached out and seized it. He leaped to his feet and brought the oar down on the head of a man who was now pummeling old Gaffer.

"Mercy, mercy, my master," whined the fellow, trying to ward off Giles' blows.

"You had no mercy, striking old Gaffer from behind," cried Giles. He struck again at the would-be thief with the oar. "Be off with you!"

The fellow sprang into his skiff. He pushed away and was quickly lost to sight among the river craft.

"The rascally thief!" The old boatman rubbed his head as Giles helped him up. "Since the farms are turned into sheep pastures, many farmers are out of work. So they roam the land, stealing. True it is that the sheep give us a fine business in wool. But England is full of beggars and thieves, alack!"

"My purse!" exclaimed Giles, feeling beneath his cloak. "It's gone!"

"Od's bodikins!" exclaimed the old man. "He took your blows while he took your purse!"

"Well, after all," reflected Giles soberly, "I had not *much* in it, though 'twas all I had! Wait, I still have the golden sovereign which Her Grace sent me, with her likeness upon it. At least I can pay you, Gaffer, for the boat ride."

"Nay, Master Giles, the Queen's man has already paid me. Look sharp now, we are coming to London Bridge."

Giles looked up at the massive arches rising before them, and the shops and dwellings four and five stories high that stood upon the bridge. He drew in his breath sharply. "Whew, Gaffer, look at that!"

The gateway arches at either end of the bridge were bordered with heads on spikes.

"A proper warning, eh, lad, to thieves and murderers and traitors!" cackled the old man. "Look lively now! We're going under the bridge, through the rapids."

As they came through on the other side Giles saw the Tower and the gallery where he had played as a little boy, high above the Tower green. And there was the water gate, the Traitor's Gate, still rimmed with bloody heads.

Giles was silent and thoughtful as they kept on down the river. Would he see little Elspeth again, he wondered. Would she be at Greenwich with the Queen, as her letter had said she might be?

" 'Sing cuckoo, sing cuckoo,' " he tried his changing voice, " 'with a folderol a lay.' "

The barge drew up at the river stairs of Greenwich Castle. Giles leaped out, cried a good-by and thanks, and took the steps three at a time. Then he remembered. He was coming to visit Her glorious Majesty, Queen Elizabeth.

"Your manners, Giles my lad, your manners!" he could fairly hear Sir Roger Ascham say. "You are going to the Court of the greatest Queen in Christendom. And Her Majesty likes gentle manners. Remember, lad, your fortune lies with the Queen."

CHAPTER ELEVEN

At the Court of Queen Elizabeth

IN A garden where Queen Elizabeth and her ladies often sat on a fair day, a pretty little girl squirmed on a marble bench. Every few minutes she jumped up to peer over the hedge toward the river.

Suddenly a barge drew up at the water stairs. "Giles!" she said softly. But how tall he had grown! As he disappeared from sight she ran back to her bench.

She spread out her billowing skirts, smoothed her flaxen curls, folded her hands, waiting. Minute after minute passed. Where was he?

Suddenly from behind, two hands were clasped over her eyes. "You're Giles," she cried. "I know it! Come now, let me see you!"

"Bother," laughed Giles, stepping from behind the bench. "You did not even wait for me to say 'Guess who?' Elspeth. My," he exclaimed, "you look pretty. You've grown since last I saw you."

"I'm nearly ten," she said demurely. She jumped up to show him—he was half again as tall as she! She threw her arms around his waist and, looking up at him, said earnestly, "And when I am sixteen, I shall marry no one but you."

Giles' cheeks grew poppy-red. "But you are only a child, Elspeth."

"I am a maid-in-waiting to Her Majesty," replied Elspeth importantly. "And I was bid to fetch Master Maris at once to the Council Hall, and later to Her gracious Majesty."

Within the hour Giles was seated beside Elspeth upon a balcony which looked down into the Council Hall. In a great thronelike chair at the far end sat the Queen herself. On one side sat the nobles of her Court. On the other were her important advisers. They were all members of Parliament who helped her govern England.

The boy gazed eagerly down. The Queen

was splendid, magnificent! A ruff of white lace framed her face, plumes and jewels circled her bright hair, her gown of purple velvet and chartreuse satin gleamed with pearls and amethysts.

"That is Sir William Cecil, her first minister, beside her," whispered Elspeth, "and on the other side is William Somers. He was King Henry's Fool, and Her Majesty sets great store by him."

"But who is the tiny woman at her feet?" whispered Giles. "She is monstrous ugly."

"That is one of Her Majesty's extraordinary women. She is the Queen's favorite woman dwarf. Her name is Thomasina," replied the little girl.

Now a silence fell over the hall, for the Queen was about to address the members of Parliament. Without rising from her throne-like chair, she began to speak.

"My Lords, my good friends all," her rich, deep voice filled the hall. "When I came to rule over you, our England was in a sorry state. Many people had been unjustly treated."

"Hear, hear!" rose from all sides of the hall.

"The poor were without work," continued the Queen. "The countryside was overrun with great bands of robbers. The highways were not safe for honest folk. Nor for coaches either, for their wheels broke in the ruts."

Everyone laughed.

The Queen smiled and went on. "There was no money in the Treasury. The debts of the Crown had not been paid. War and invasion threatened us on every side. Scotland, France, and Spain all wanted to seize England."

The Queen paused and the people waited in silence.

"We are trying to change all that," she said. "The debts of the Crown have been paid. There is money in the Treasury. Peace has been kept both abroad and at home. Only with peace, my Lords and Commons, can England prosper. No war, my Lords, no war! England shall be for the English.

"With peace and agreement at home, We propose to take care of our poor and idle. Let those who are old and ill and unable to work be taken care of by the parishes in which they live. But the idle vagabonds—" The Queen stopped speaking. She looked from one side of the hall to the other, as if to test what her listeners were thinking. "The idle vagabonds," she repeated, "shall be made to work in houses of correction. Others may work on our roads, which are yet only muddy paths."

"Hear, hear!" rose the answer from the hall.

"And for those good folk who want work, it will be Our care to furnish it for them," cried the Queen.

"Hear, hear," echoed the Fool. "Now many among us who never worked before shall have to work. Oh me, oh my!"

When the laughter had died the Queen went on. "From now on we shall not send our woolens to Italy to be dyed, nor to Flanders to be woven. We shall do this here at home, in England. You know that already our farm wives are spinning, weaving, and dyeing our own English wool. And our fine broadcloth has no equal."

Now the Queen rose and stood before them. Her voice rang through the hall and to the lofty paneled ceiling.

"We are building a navy, and there are many merchant vessels. I say that in Our day London will become the greatest city, the greatest market, of the world."

Sir William Cecil, standing just at the Queen's shoulder, nodded and smiled his approval.

"The cottons of India," said Her Majesty, "the silks and brocades of the Far East, the gold and sugar of the New World, will pour into our port."

Such cheers as went up! Elizabeth, smiling

and nodding, raised her jeweled white hand for silence once more. "These are the rewards of peace, my people," she cried.

"God save our Queen!" The shouts were deafening.

As the Queen seated herself, a messenger entered the hall. Beckoned forward, he knelt at Her Majesty's feet. She took from him a letter, and read. In a moment she was on her feet, her eyes flashing fire.

"Hear this, my Lords, and gentlemen," she cried. "It comes from Our Scottish cousin, Mary Stuart. Her husband, the French King, has died, and she wishes to return to Scotland through England. She asks for safe passage. What is your will? Shall we welcome one who has already laid claim to the throne of England?"

An angry murmur rose through the hall. A young noble spoke.

"She will stir up trouble wherever she goes. She looks to Spanish Philip to put her on England's throne. We have learned the blessings of peace and of English rule. Let Mary Stuart give up her claims to England."

"Hear, hear!" cried the merchants and Commons.

"Then we shall inform Our royal cousin that she may have a safe escort through Our realm, if she will renounce forever her claims to the throne of England," said Elizabeth.

And now the young Queen's voice was gentle and tender and sincere. "Nothing," she said, "nothing, no worldly thing under the sun, is so dear to me as the love and good will of my subjects."

There was no doubt but that Elizabeth's people loved her, for there was such cheering as almost raised the roof. The Council was over. Giles and Elspeth had listened spellbound.

"Why does Queen Mary of the Scots claim Her Majesty's throne?" Elspeth tugged at Giles' doublet.

"Because her grandmother was sister to our Queen's father, King Henry the Eighth," said Giles. "But come, let us go to the gardens. I must have flowers for Her gracious Highness."

The gardener gave Giles leave to pick the blooms he wished, and Elspeth ran along by his side. "Do you think our Queen will marry, Giles?" she asked curiously. "She has many suitors. King Philip of Spain himself wants to wed her. I think that is because he wants to have power in England again. But our Queen has refused to marry him, and he is becoming our bitter enemy."

"How do you know all this, Elspeth?" asked Giles. "I think you must have a clever pair of ears on your pretty little head!"

"I cannot help hearing when people speak before me, Giles," Elspeth pouted. "And besides, Thomasina, the woman dwarf, is my great friend and tells me much. The Queen loves Thomasina, and never whips her, as she does some of the ladies when they are slow, or forward."

"And what else have you learned, little ears?" laughed Giles, as he clipped a lovely rosebud.

"There *is* something else!" Elspeth stopped suddenly and laid a finger across her lips.

"And what is that?" Giles clipped his last rose and drew Elspeth behind a hedge where they would not be overheard. They sat down and she put her lips against his ear.

"There are plots against Her Grace. There are some who *do* want to put Mary of Scotland on the throne." She nodded solemnly. "And they have put their people *right here in the Court!* Thomasina knows. But she is afraid to tell. And Her Majesty is so brave, so careless of danger, she suspects none."

"But this is terrible, Elspeth," said Giles. "You must tell Sir William Cecil!"

"The Queen's first minister would never believe a little girl like me," whispered Elspeth, her eyes round with fear. "We could not even get to him."

"We can reach his aide," said Giles. "Come along." He caught her hand. "Wait until Sir William's secret service hears of this! You know the names of those who are plotting? Good! We must hurry."

CHAPTER TWELVE

Plotters in the Palace

ELSPETH trembled as she curtsied before the Queen's first minister. Here she was actually in the private chamber of the great Sir William Cecil!

"Don't be afraid, my child," Sir William said, looking at her kindly. "Now, tell me what this is all about."

He listened gravely to the child's story.

"So, you heard all this while you were playing in the garden?"

"I did, Your Lordship," Elspeth nodded. "I was hiding from a little boy named Monarcho, in a great urn in the far garden, when suddenly two men spoke. The first one offered the guard some money to let two men into the Queen's bedchamber. They were to stab her.

Then those who are for Scottish Mary were to rise up and seize the palace."

"What did the guard say?" asked Sir William Cecil.

"He said, 'We cannot murder the Queen. She is too strong in England. But when you have seized her, we can drive Sir William Cecil from power.' And he said, 'And then we can force the Queen to name Mary of Scotland as heir to the throne of England.'"

"And what did the other man say?" asked Sir William.

"He said," Elspeth's eyes were wide with excitement. "He said, 'No. We can never force Elizabeth to do that. Too many of the English people are against it. But King Philip and the Spanish are going to make Mary the Queen of England. Be ready!' "

"Who was the guard?" Sir William's face was stern.

"It was—" Elspeth went close and whispered in Sir William Cecil's ear.

"Heh, one of those whom she has trusted. Well, you are a right loyal little maid," smiled Her Majesty's minister. "You and Giles have done your Queen and your country a true service this day. Her Highness will not forget. And have no fear. None shall know. No harm shall come to you."

And so the enemies of the Queen were stopped, but only for the time being. Beautiful Queen Mary of Scotland would not give up her claim to the English throne and was not allowed to travel through England. Even so, she reached her own country safely by sea, and her people rejoiced because she had come home from France to rule them.

Months passed and the young Scottish Queen married her cousin, Lord Darnley. A son was born whom they named James. Then a shocking thing happened. Lord Darnley was murdered!

Many people believed that Mary herself had helped plan this murder. When she married the man who was believed to be the murderer, thousands of her subjects turned against her. She was taken prisoner and sent to a castle on the island of Lochleven. There she was forced to sign a paper, giving up the throne of Scotland to her baby son, James.

For eleven months Mary was imprisoned on the lonely island. Then, with the help of some faithful followers, she escaped by boat and fled to England. The news of her escape quickly reached the palace of Queen Elizabeth.

"Mary must not be allowed to remain in this country, Your Majesty," Sir William Cecil said to the Queen. "Her friends will gather around her and continue plotting to get Your

Grace's throne. As long as Mary lives, your life is in danger."

"Send her back to Scotland," urged Elizabeth's other ministers. "Allow her to go to France. Or give orders that she be killed."

But Elizabeth would do none of these things. Instead she commanded that Mary should be kept in England as a prisoner. So the Scottish queen was lodged in first one castle and then another. Although she was well guarded, her presence in England worried all who loved Elizabeth. Indeed, the Queen herself was often uneasy about her royal prisoner, but she had a multitude of other things to think about.

Many princes came to England to woo Her Majesty. They sent messengers to her with costly gifts. These ambassadors were royally entertained with splendid banquets, with music, and with plays. They were showered with presents.

The Queen wore a new gown every day. Her learning astonished everyone. She spoke in Italian and French and—to the most learned men—in Latin. She danced a gay coranto and sang and played the harpsichord for the company. But she sent all her suitors and their ambassadors home again after a time.

"I shall marry no one," she told herself. "I am wedded to England."

She smiled as she said it, for she was pleased with her country and her people. For some years now England had been at peace. The people were working and trading, not fighting. So the country was ever growing richer and more powerful.

Spain also had been growing richer. Soon after Columbus had discovered America, Spanish ships had sailed there and Spanish explorers had discovered gold. Then the Spaniards had seized Mexico, Panama, Peru, and the islands in the Caribbean sea.

They had conquered the Indians living in these lands and forced them to work like slaves. From the gold mines in the New World had come more gold than had ever been seen before. And every Spanish ship which returned from America was loaded with treasure.

Sometimes when those ships neared home they were attacked by English sailors. There were fierce fights at sea. Now and then the

Spanish won. But more often the English captured the treasure and carried it home. Part of this treasure was always given to the Queen.

"And it is right that we should take it," Giles Maris told Elspeth, as they sat one evening by the river. "King Philip of Spain uses the gold from America to build armies so that some day he may conquer England. So the less he gets, the better off we'll be."

For a moment Elspeth did not speak. She was fourteen now and wished Giles to realize that she was almost a young lady, so she chose her words carefully.

" 'Tis a pity," she said at last, "that we have no great English navigators to bring home gold from America."

"But we have," laughed Giles. "Have you never heard of Hawkins or Frobisher? Hawkins has already made two trips to the New World. Even now he is getting ready to set forth on another voyage. A young man named Drake will be one of his captains."

"Who told you of all this?" asked Elspeth.

"Why, I myself talked with Francis Drake today when he brought letters from Hawkins to our Queen. Some day Drake plans to lead an expedition of his own across the ocean and perhaps—" Giles hesitated.

"Perhaps what?" prompted Elspeth.

"If Her gracious Majesty will give me permission, perhaps I will go with him," Giles said with a smile.

CHAPTER THIRTEEN

Francis Drake Returns

GREAT excitement and bustle filled Whitehall Palace. Tiring women and maids ran hither and thither in the Queen's apartment. They fetched a hundred dresses from her closets for her to choose from.

For Francis Drake, the great voyager, was home from Panama. He would arrive that very afternoon. Word had come up from Portsmouth that his voyage had been highly successful.

The Queen was in an excellent humor.

"Elspeth, my very pet," she said, tapping the girl affectionately with her fan, "remember, Our favorite, Giles Maris, returns with Captain Drake this day." She looked sharply at Elspeth.

"Ah, Giles will have forgotten me, Your Grace." Elspeth blushed in spite of herself. "Six years have passed. Why, I am over twenty, and Giles is a grown man. Giles thinks only of Your Majesty and of serving you, I vow."

The Queen smiled in delight. Sweet words pleased her much, as Elspeth well knew. Curtsying deeply, Elspeth backed away from Her Majesty's presence.

Elspeth was trembling with excitement. What would Giles think of her? Would he remember the silly promise she had made so long ago? That she would marry him? But she was only nine when she made that promise, and he fourteen.

Soon after she had become fourteen, Elspeth had been called to Hatfield, and had remained there for five long years. When both her parents died the Queen had brought her back to Court.

But before she returned Giles had gone off with Francis Drake, a-voyaging to the New World. He was to be eyes and ears on the long journey, and Queen's historian. And Elspeth had been eyes and ears here in the palace, watching and listening for plotters.

Now Elspeth looked at herself in the glass. Her flaxen curls had deepened to the color of ripe corn. A little blue velvet bonnet, sewn with pearls, framed her lovely face. Her gown was blue taffeta, puffed and shirred and embroidered with rosebuds.

Suddenly from afar came the sound of trumpets, the clatter of hoofs. Nearer and nearer! The courtyard rang with voices.

"They have come, they have come! Francis Drake is home from the Indies!"

Down the corridors swept the Queen. Her ladies followed. Doors opened before her. She entered the great hall, and seated herself upon her throne, magnificent, her nobles around her. Again there was a sound of trumpets. The outer doors were thrown open.

"Captain Francis Drake!" and down the long halls the name echoed, "Captain Francis Dra-aa-ke!"

The great navigator entered. He was a commanding figure with a pleasant open face, a pointed beard, and bushy, curling hair. He carried a helmet and his steel corselet showed beneath a velvet doublet.

But Elspeth's eyes darted among his follow-

"Francis Drake is home from the Indies!"

ers, searching for one face. Giles, where was he? Giles! Could it be that he had not returned from the sea? For a moment Elspeth's heart stood still.

Then she saw him, standing among the sunbrowned men. He was gazing straight ahead —at the Queen. He was not looking for anyone he knew then. He had forgotten her.

But now the Queen was speaking, welcoming the great seafarer home. "Whence have you come, Captain Francis? Tell us what has befallen you during your voyage. Is it true that you have returned with stores of silver and gold?"

Captain Drake knelt and kissed Her Majesty's hand. "It is true, Your gracious Highness," he replied, rising at her command. "I have been to the Spanish settlement, Nombre de Dios, in Panama. And I bring back more silver and gold than will pay for the voyage many times over."

At a sign from Captain Drake, his men advanced two by two, bearing between them great mahogany chests. The Court drew breath, and everyone craned forward, even the Queen, as the chests were opened.

There lay gleaming bars of solid gold and silver. One entire casket was filled with great pearls, with uncut opals and emeralds, and with curiously wrought gold ornaments.

"But this is nothing," cried Drake. "I shall return to the New World where there is still more treasure. With Your Grace's favor and the help of God, I shall reap some of that golden harvest which the Spanish found there. And which they bring back to Philip so that he may pay his armies to wage war in Europe."

"Good Captain Drake," cried the Queen, her eyes flashing. "Nobly said! You speak of other treasure. Tell us, pray, where can it be found?"

"In a country called Peru, Your Grace," replied Drake eagerly. "Before I left Panama I became most friendly with the Indians. I treated them kindly. And they showed me from a treetop the waters of that great sea, the Pacific. None but the Spaniards have ever sailed on that vast blue ocean. They have built their ships upon its shores, first carrying their supplies across Panama at its narrowest point. And they have found great treasure in Peru."

"What is to prevent our doing the same?" cried the Queen, her voice deep and challenging. "Our ships are equal to theirs. Nay, they are better than any."

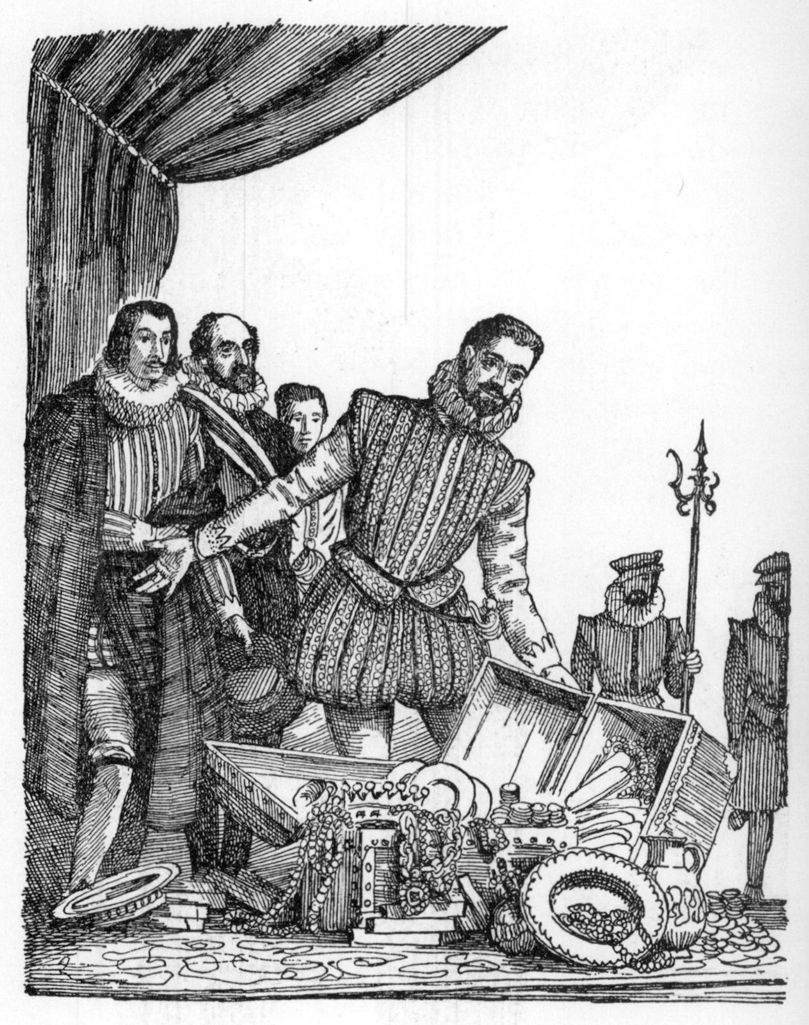

"So is our seamanship, Your Majesty," replied Francis Drake stoutly. "There is nothing to prevent us from going there. I threw myself upon my knees before God, and I

prayed for Him to grant me life, and allow me to sail an English vessel upon those seas."

"And with God's help and Our own, you shall do so, brave Captain," replied the Queen. "If indeed great treasure lies there, let us seek some of it."

"Your Grace," Francis Drake said earnestly, "this gold and silver which I have brought you now is as nothing compared to the riches of the mines of Peru. I can promise all who help to fit me out with ships and supplies, that they shall be repaid many times over. This I swear in all good faith."

"And in that we trust, most faithful of captains." The Queen smiled radiantly upon Francis Drake. And when Her Grace smiled and spoke warmly, none could resist her.

Now the audience was over. Elizabeth gave a sign that the company might talk. Elspeth felt eyes upon her, but she dared not look. She waited among the Queen's ladies, and there Giles came and found her.

"Elspeth! It is you, is it not?"

"Yes, Giles," she whispered. For a moment she could hardly speak, she was so happy. "Have I changed so, then?"

"You are grown," he smiled, "into a beautiful maid."

"What has happened to you in these years?" Elspeth smiled back. She led him to a wide window seat. "Let us sit here, and you can tell me of your adventures."

Giles laughed. "I saw no lambs growing on trees," he said, "as some travelers have told. Nor giants nor dwarfs, either, though we have both here at home! But I saw fearsome dragon-like monsters, with horny skins and wide, evil grins. They could bite a man in two.

"And I saw Indians draw smoke from a pipe into their mouths, and breathe it forth from their nostrils as though they were on fire within. But here, here is something I have brought for you."

He drew out a beautiful necklace and bracelet to match—his share of the Panama voyage. And before anyone could see, he had kissed her. And before they left the window seat Elspeth had promised to marry Giles. "If Her Grace, the Queen, so permits," she said. "For Her Majesty will not allow her maids nor her courtiers to marry without her consent."

The Queen was in a happy mood and gave not only her consent, but a beautiful wedding feast to her young favorites.

These were quiet times in England now. And prosperous ones. Queen Elizabeth would leave London during the heat of summer and go with all her Court to the country. She visited often at the great estates of her wealthy nobles.

On a warm July day in the year 1575, a royal procession wound its way over the rough roads of the English countryside. The Queen rode a white horse, and with her rode all her ladies, her dwarfs and jesters, her Moorish boy, Monarcho, and Thomasina, the tiny woman. The countryfolk cheered the gorgeous procession.

They were bound for Kenilworth Castle, the great home of the Earl of Leicester. And there they were splendidly entertained. Plays and pageants and tournaments, fireworks and feasts and games, went on for week after week.

At the end of the visit the great magician Merlin looked in his magic crystal ball and foretold the Queen's fortune: "A long reign, such glory as no queen has ever had, and great riches—which will come from across the seas."

A long reign! Glory! Riches! Yes, all this and more. And yet even then the seeds of great danger were sprouting.

CHAPTER FOURTEEN

Queen Bess Is in Danger

IT WAS a raw day of 1580. In the small inner chamber of Sir William Cecil's study, Her Highness the Queen stood warming her hands at a cheerful fire. She and Sir William had been talking about Mary Stuart of Scotland.

"As long as she is in England there will be unrest," said Cecil.

He pulled his handsome velvet cap down tightly and retied it under his chin. He was getting older and felt the cold.

"My dear Cecil," said the Queen, "today Mary seems no more than a thorn in my finger. We have other matters to trouble us."

"Yes, Philip of Spain has taken Portugal." Sir William rubbed his cold blue hands before the fire. "His armies grow stronger hour by hour. I wish that Drake were here. But he has been gone nearly three years, and who knows when, or whether, he will ever return!"

"Drake will come back!" cried Elizabeth. "I'd stake my life on it. He is a magnificent navigator. And the greatest sea fighter of all."

The words were hardly out of her mouth when the bells began to toll in London, and the town crier could be heard calling his news in the streets. Within a few moments a messenger knelt before the Queen.

"Francis Drake has returned, Your Majesty, and his ships lie at anchor in Plymouth Harbor. He has sailed clear around the world!"

Around the world! It seemed hard to believe, yet it was true. Francis Drake had sailed from England with five ships. Now he had only one left—a little vessel called *The Golden Hind*. It had carried England's flag across a sea where no English flag had ever been before. The people of London went wild when they heard this news. The story of Drake's voyage spread quickly, and soon people in many parts of England were discussing it.

"Drake has crossed the Pacific Ocean!"

"He's sailed all the way around the world. They say he's returned with a ship filled with treasure."

"Aye, but he's little better than a pirate. Have you not heard how he burned Spanish settlements in the New World and robbed Spanish ships off the coasts of Chile and Peru?"

"No matter! The Spanish have robbed our ships, too, and captured our sailors. Drake's a brave man."

So the talk ran, and when Francis Drake sailed the little *Golden Hind* up the Thames River, excited men, women, and children crowded to the shore to see it. Then the great navigator appeared before the Queen and her Court.

The nobles and merchants who had given money to outfit Drake's fine ships could scarcely believe their ears when he told them of the treasure he had brought home. He had loaded his bark with gold dust, silver ingots, jewels, silks, spices, and other rare things.

"There is more than four thousand times profit for every penny which was put into the voyage, Your Majesty," Drake reported. "And to Your Highness goes one tenth of the whole."

The Queen was delighted with this news. But King Philip of Spain was furious when he learned of Drake's capture of his gold. He was even more angry when he heard that the Queen had visited the *Golden Hind* and knighted Francis Drake. Drake was *Sir* Francis now, and the Queen wore his jewels in her crown.

Months passed and there came to the Queen's Court a young captain by the name of Walter Raleigh. From the first moment Elizabeth laid eyes on him, she liked him.

He was not only tall, but handsome. He was a poet. He could dance and play an excellent game of chess or cards with the Queen. He was courtly and gracious and beautifully dressed. But most important of all, he was filled with great ideas.

"Your gracious Majesty," he said to the Queen, "it is not enough that we capture *wealth* from the New World. Let us plant a bit of England there. Let us send colonists, supplied with all needful things, to build another England."

"But America is a wild and savage place," cried the Queen. "And ships cost money. Have you forgotten Frobisher's expedition?"

No, Walter Raleigh had not forgotten. Martin Frobisher, a brave sea captain, had tried to start a settlement in the New World on an island to the north of Labrador. But he had failed and had returned to England.

"Frobisher's expedition cost me a pretty penny," the Queen went on. "And I will not give you leave to cross the ocean, good Walter. I wish to keep you here at Court. Come, let us walk in the garden and talk no more about colonies in the New World."

So they walked in the beautiful rose gardens of the palace and spoke no more that day about America. But Walter Raleigh did not give up his idea of planting a colony there.

Although the Queen still refused to let him leave her, she agreed at last that he might send two ships to America. The men on the ships were to explore the coast.

"If they find land which is not inhabited by Christian people and which does not belong to any Christian prince, it shall be yours," the Queen told Raleigh. "And there you may send people to start an English settlement."

So it was that on an April day, Walter Raleigh watched two little ships sail down the Thames River, bound for the New World.

Five months later they returned. Their captains had brought back skins, pearls, and two copper-colored Indians. They also brought news of a fair warm land, and an island called Roanoke on which a settlement might well be started.

The Queen decided then that the new land should be named Virginia and that her good Walter should be knighted. She still refused to let him go to the New World. But she allowed him to send a fleet of seven ships to Roanoke. The ships carried more than a hundred colonists and were commanded by a man named Richard Grenville.

Meanwhile all was not going well in England. It seemed as though there was no end of plotting to kill the Queen and to put the country under the rule of Spain.

"Your Majesty is in greater danger this moment than ever before," said the Queen's secretary one day. "Philip is plotting with the French to invade England. His soldiers have marched across Holland. They plan to cross the Channel. And he has sent money to a group of men here at home who intend to seize and murder Your Grace."

"How do you know this, Walsingham?" The Queen rose from her chair and began to stride up and down the room, as was her habit.

"Your Grace, I have suspected these men for some time and have set spies to watch them. One of the men has been arrested. A man named Ballard." Walsingham wiped his brow with a square of fine linen.

"We stretched him on the rack," he continued, "and when his joints began to crack he confessed everything. Mary of Scotland knows of the plot and approves of it. She has written letters in secret to the leader of the plotters."

"And who is this leader?" asked the Queen.

"Anthony Babington, Your Grace."

"Babington!" The Queen repeated the name in surprise. "Why, he was here in my Court for two full years." She spoke sadly. "I thought he was loyal to me. And Mary of Scotland has agreed that I shall be murdered?"

"That is so, Your Grace," replied Walsingham. "We have her letters to prove it."

The Queen turned quickly. "What of Babington?" she asked. "Has he, too, been arrested?"

"Not yet. He has escaped us, as have the other conspirators. But every effort is being made to find them. And with Your Grace's permission, Mary of Scotland shall be more closely guarded. If Philip can have you killed, he will put her on the throne."

"Ha, Philip has been trying to do that for

many years!" the Queen exclaimed. "But we have our seamen and our ships to protect us from invasion. See that Babington and the other conspirators are found, good Walsingham. And leave me now. I have need to think."

Bowing low, Walsingham withdrew. For some time Elizabeth stood at her window, gazing out at the wide green lawns which lay warm in the soft August sunshine. It was difficult for her to believe that Mary of Scotland would really wish to see her dead. Or that anyone who had been in her Court would want to murder her.

Although she was now past fifty, Elizabeth did not show her age. She enjoyed life. She loved to dance, to play at cards, to ride, to play her spinet. She loved fine clothes and pageants and the compliments of her courtiers.

"But better than all these things, I love England," she thought. "The welfare of my people and the safety of the throne come first. And, with God's help, neither Philip nor Scottish Mary shall ever rule this land."

CHAPTER FIFTEEN

"Off with Her Head!"

BONFIRES blazed in the streets of London. Bells rang from every steeple. People shouted, danced for joy, and marched up and down to the music of tabors and drums.

"Hey, what's going on here?" cried an old farmer who had come to town to sell his sheep.

"The traitors have been caught!" yelled a small boy in reply.

"What traitors?"

"Babington," shouted the small boy's father, "and those others who plotted against our dear Queen. They'll all be hanged and Mary of Scotland—"

"May she hang, too!" cried a cobbler who had left his bench.

"Down with Mary!" yelled the crowd.

"She'd try to rule England, would she? Off with her head!"

All London was in an uproar. In old Cheapside Street a group of merchants were discussing the capture of the traitors, and the threat to the Queen's life.

"Gentlemen," cried a richly dressed merchant, "never have we been so rich and prosperous! And why? Because of our Queen, Her gracious Majesty, Elizabeth, God bless her. She has kept peace in this land. We want no foreign ruler here. No Mary of Scotland! No Philip of Spain! England for the English, I say. Down with the traitors! God bless our Queen!"

"Down with the traitors! God bless our good Queen Bess!" The cries rang out again and again in all parts of the city that day. Not until evening did the people begin to return to their homes.

When the light had faded, a group of writers and poets gathered around a table in the Mermaid Tavern, as was their custom.

"What think you, gentlemen?" asked Francis Bacon, a young lawyer who had just been elected to Parliament. "An end to Babington and the other traitors does not mean an end to Philip of Spain, does it?"

"Could we hold a Spanish invasion off?" asked a young poet, Christopher Marlowe by name. "You, Walter, what do you say?"

"England has no army," Raleigh replied. "There are scarcely enough troops to patrol the Scottish border, nor to keep the peace in Ireland. But it is Spain on the seas that we have to fear. And Spain's hold on the New World."

"You are not only a poet and a courtier, Sir Walter," said Francis Bacon, "but a statesman and an explorer as well. Tell us how your Virginia colonies go."

"Not too well, I fear," replied Raleigh sadly. He took a long draw on his long silver-stemmed pipe and blew out a cloud of fragrant smoke.

"You know that the two ships which I sent out two years ago brought back two Indians, and acquainted us with the use of tobacco. The ships found a fair land at Roanoke Island, and for this the Queen knighted me."

"And made you Captain of the Queen's Guards last year," reminded Bacon with envy.

The tall handsome Sir Walter was rich; he was always elegantly dressed in satins and jewels which would have bought a whole estate.

"Her Majesty rewarded me generously," exclaimed Raleigh. "But the colonists I sent out with Grenville last year met with hard luck. I know that I could have helped them, if Her Majesty had allowed me to go with them."

"What was the trouble, think you?" asked young Marlowe sympathetically.

"It was not the Indians," said Walter Raleigh quickly. "Most of them were friendly. But the gentlemen did not know how to work. After Grenville left them and came home to get supplies, many of them died. Later the rest returned to England with Sir Francis Drake, who stopped at Roanoke on his last voyage."

"But Grenville went back to Virginia with more colonists, did he not?" asked Bacon.

"Yes, he reached Roanoke soon after Drake's ships had sailed. Of course he found no settlers there and most of the new colonists were afraid to remain. Only fifteen agreed to stay. But I am planning a well-fitted company to sail next year to join them. I shall not give up. Some day we will have new ports in the

New World with which to trade. You will see."

He puffed on his silver pipe. Young Francis Bacon smiled.

"The trade in this new tobacco which your ships brought from America is already successful," he said kindly. "Everyone wants to smoke because the fashionable Sir Walter does."

Raleigh laughed, and springing to his feet, he raised his glass. "Let us drink a toast to Her Majesty," he cried, "and to her new province, Virginia! Long live the Queen!"

As the gentlemen seated themselves after the toast was finished, the great sea captain, Martin Frobisher, joined the company.

"There is still some celebrating in the streets, because the plotters have been captured," he said, pulling his chair up to the table. "The people do truly love our Queen."

"And truly hate those who try to do her harm," said Francis Bacon. "Mary of Scotland must die for her part in this plot. All England will demand it."

Indeed, the people throughout England did demand the death of all the traitors. Within a few weeks Babington and his plotters were hanged. And Mary of Scotland had been put under close guard in Fotheringay Castle many miles from London.

There she was tried, and found guilty of plotting against the Queen, and sentenced to death. Only one thing was needed before the sentence could be carried out. Queen Elizabeth must sign her cousin's death warrant. And that she could not bring herself to do. For Mary's execution might bring more harm than good to England.

Weeks passed and still the warrant remained unsigned, though Elizabeth's advisers begged her again and again to write her name across the paper. One winter day they met with her in her council chamber in Greenwich.

"Your Grace," said Walsingham earnestly, "there will always be plots against your life as long as Mary of Scotland remains alive. And one of these plots may succeed."

"Mary has been tried and found guilty," Sir William Cecil reminded her. "The warrant for her death, Your Majesty, waits only for you to sign."

Elizabeth looked down at the evidence

which had been laid before her. Then, raising her eyes, she looked out of the window, over the Thames River. Far in the distance she could see the gray turrets of the Tower. The Tower! How near she herself had come to death there!

"I cannot sign the warrant!" The Queen rose from her chair and paced nervously about the room.

"Your Majesty," said Cecil, "as long as Mary lives, England remains in danger of invasion. Even now Spain is preparing for war. My spies bring word that the Spanish are gathering such a fleet as the world has never seen before."

"It may already be too late," Walsingham added. "But with Mary out of the way, England will at least be free of plotters within the country."

"Then give me the warrant for her execution!" cried the Queen at last.

She signed it quickly and threw down the pen. But she gave no orders to have the warrant carried out, though she knew it was her duty. For she still could not bear to take the blame for Mary's death. When she heard, some time later, that Mary of Scotland had been beheaded at Fotheringay, she wept bitterly.

"Who sent that warrant to Fotheringay?" she cried. "I never meant that it should be

sent. I never meant that Mary should be killed. Who sent the warrant?"

It was her ministers, of course, who had sent the warrant to Fotheringay. But the Queen placed most of the blame for this on one of her secretaries, a young man named Davison. Quite unfairly she ordered him arrested and imprisoned in the Tower.

Meanwhile people throughout England celebrated joyfully because the traitor—Mary of Scotland—had lost her head. And Spain went on preparing to make war because King Philip was determined to rule England.

CHAPTER SIXTEEN

The Spanish Armada

REPORTS came daily of the tremendous fleet that Philip was building. And so the dauntless Drake at once set out to "singe the King of Spain's beard," as he said. And singe it he did.

He darted in with his swift little ships to all the ports of Spain. He burned ships and storehouses full of supplies. Philip would not be able to invade England *that* year!

But Philip's great fleet, the "Spanish Armada," went right on building, and his armies grew stronger day by day. However, the English were not waiting idly. Elizabeth had never declared war, but now she was ready to defend the beloved English soil to the last ditch.

"This must be a sea battle," cried Sir Francis Drake at a meeting of the council. "We cannot defeat the Spanish soldiers on land. Our soldiers are few and untrained. They have never seen a real battle. But our sailors have fought the Spanish on two oceans. We must have more ships, Your Majesty!"

More ships were made ready and all England prepared to meet the great Armada.

Lord Howard of Effingham was in command of the Navy, with those brave sea dogs, Drake, Hawkins, and Frobisher, helping. The Queen herself helped to outfit thirty vessels, and raised a large army.

"Let twenty thousand soldiers be placed along our southern coast," she ordered, "and put footsoldiers and a thousand horsemen near the mouth of the Thames."

This was soon done, and other soldiers were stationed between the coast and London, to defend the Queen in case the Spanish landed. Elizabeth herself drove down to the camps in her new coach to cheer and encourage these men.

Beacons were placed all along the coast to give warning whenever the Spanish appeared. And then, on the 29th day of July in the year

1588, the Armada was sighted. At once the warning light flashed from beacon to beacon.

Sir Francis Drake was bowling with his captains at Plymouth Hoe when— "The Spanish are coming," rose the lookout's cry.

"Let them come!" cried Drake, and he cast another ball down the deck. "There'll be time enough to finish our game and beat the Spaniards too!"

Up the Channel came the great Armada.

"Let them pass by, let them pass," ordered the Admiral, Lord Howard. "We shall attack from the rear."

Giles Maris, now a handsome bearded captain, stood at Drake's elbow. "The wind is from the southwest," said Drake. "We shall have it at our backs as we follow them."

When the Spanish ships had passed by, the English ships put out from Plymouth Harbor. They cleared Ramsgate and tacked westward, coming up behind the Spaniards.

"We must stop them before they reach Flanders," said Drake grimly. "Spanish troops are waiting there—the best fighting armies in all Europe—to join the Spanish fleet and land on our shores."

Now the English began to close in on the rear of the Armada. At last they could really see the enemy. What a sight! A great half-moon of monstrous caravels blocked the Channel.

"They outnumber us by a hundred ships!" cried Hawkins.

There ahead lay the greatest fleet ever gathered together in the memory of man. There were the largest ships ever built. The English counted some 160 Spanish vessels, all told; 92 huge galleons, 30 frigates, 30 transport ships for horsemen, and four galleys. Even the smaller ships had 50 guns apiece. And in the Spanish fleet were thousands of soldiers and nearly ten thousand sailors. But the Duke of Sidonia, who commanded the fleet, had never been to sea before in all his life!

The English had only 80 ships, most of them small. Yet they carried more and heavier guns than the Spanish. The wind was at their backs and they fairly flew up within firing range. And now it was seen how much more easily the English ships were handled.

Boom, boo-oom, boo-oom, the guns roared over the waves. The English seadogs were showing their teeth! Not only were the English ships better, the gunners were better. They fired four shots to the Spaniards' one, hitting the high, top-heavy Spanish galleons right amidships, or at the water line. The cracking and crashing of masts, the thunder of guns, the cries of the wounded, made a frightful din.

But the Spanish cannon, which were stationed high on the lofty decks, could do little damage. They shot through the top rigging of the British ships.

"We'll pluck their feathers one by one,"

cried Drake as the English sank galleon after galleon.

Day after day the English fleet drove the Spanish up the Channel. Soon many Spanish ships were leaking and gravely disabled. The Armada sailed into Calais on the coast of France and anchored there.

"We shall send in fireships and drive them out," said the English captains.

When the Spaniards saw the blazing fireships coming, they became frightened. Cutting their cables, they put out to sea again.

"Now," said Drake and Frobisher to Admi-

ral Howard, "we must keep them out of Flanders."

There was a terrible fight off Gravelines, and the Armada was driven on farther up the Channel. Then a wild storm arose. The wind blew the heavy Spanish galleons right past Flanders and the Spanish soldiers who were waiting there. Part of the Armada was almost wrecked on the flats of Holland. But on swept the galleons, helpless before the wind, straight into the raging North Sea.

The great Spanish ships were driven on the rocks off Scotland and Ireland. Some of the Spanish thought that the rounded cliffs on the Irish coast were fortress towers. They sailed in close to fire on them and were dashed to pieces on the shore. What the waves and rocks did not break up, English guns did. And so the great battle was finished.

The storm had come just in time, for the English were running out of powder, bullets, and cannonballs. Only fifty-four galleons were able to get back to Spain. But if a single English ship was lost, it was not reported.

There was great rejoicing throughout England at news of this tremendous victory. Now

English privateers became more daring than ever. They thought it only fair to capture Spanish treasure ships and so to keep Spain down—Spain, whose King Philip had plotted for so long to seize England and murder the Queen.

At last England had become truly Mistress of the Seas. She could trade freely in the West Indies. And the English began to think of building another England in the New World. The Queen herself lent an ear to those who wanted to send out colonists. But Walter Raleigh was having a hard time trying to plant English towns in America.

CHAPTER SEVENTEEN

The Golden Days

SIR WALTER RALEIGH paced up and down the palace hall, waiting for an audience with his Queen. He was elegantly dressed as usual, with diamonds on his fingers and in his garter buckles.

He knew that the Queen loved finery at her Court. He wanted very much to please her, for he hoped that she would consent to his sending more ships to America. Perhaps she might even allow him to sail to the New World himself. When he was shown into Her Majesty's presence, he knelt and kissed her hand.

"What news of your colony, Sir Walter?" asked the Queen, motioning to him to rise.

"Nothing, Your Grace," Raleigh replied

unhappily. "You remember that Grenville left fifteen men there after the first colonists had come home with Francis Drake?"

"I remember," replied Elizabeth a bit impatiently. "And then you sent another expedition under John White. He left one hundred and seventeen colonists on Roanoke and then came home for supplies. When he returned to Roanoke, he found the colonists gone."

"True, Your Majesty."

"Your Indian savages killed them!" exclaimed the Queen.

Walter Raleigh shook his head. "It is difficult for me to believe that," he said. "White found that the colonists had left their homes in good order. They had taken their guns and tools. I believe that they moved somewhere else and—"

"And you want to search for them. Is that not so, my dear Sir Walter?" The Queen smiled kindly. But still she would not let Raleigh sail to America, though ships were sent out to search for the lost colonists.

The following year, however, the Queen agreed that Walter Raleigh should sail as captain of a small fleet, to Panama and the West

Indies. But Raleigh, the favorite of the Queen, had fallen in love. And the night before he sailed, he was married without Her Majesty's permission to one of her court ladies.

The Queen was furious when she learned of this marriage. She sent a fast ship after the fleet to bring Raleigh back. Then she ordered that both he and his bride should be imprisoned in the Tower. And there they stayed, without even seeing each other, for four long months.

Often Raleigh thought of his little fleet which had gone on to Panama without him. One morning early in September he was suddenly freed from the Tower and taken to the port of Dartmouth.

The fleet had come home and had brought a tremendous treasure ship which had been captured off the island of Flores. It was so richly loaded that the crews and captains were fighting over it, each man trying to get more than his share of treasure.

Part of the treasure belonged to the Queen. She felt that no one could save it for her but Raleigh.

"Only you, Raleigh, can manage the crew,"

said young Robert Cecil as they were rowed out to the ship. "Look there! What a sight!"

There she lay, the great Portugese ship, so large that it had taken ten English ships to haul her into harbor. She was still blood-stained, and listed heavily to one side. Seven decks high she was, sixty-five feet long, and filled to the rail with treasure! Sailors crowded her decks. Shouts of joy and welcome rose as they recognized Walter Raleigh.

"You've taken a magnificent prize," cried Raleigh when he had boarded the ship. "All credit to the captors. But let the looting stop! Come now, men, it must be fairly divided. To each his share."

A grinning sailor spilled a string of pearls into Raleigh's hand. Others gave him more pearls, rubies, golden bracelets, and pieces of carved ivory which they had stowed away in their pockets. There were bales of silk, chests of precious spices, amber, silver, gold, and musk. Much of it was still untouched.

All was counted and evenly divided. Then Raleigh added his own share and that of his brother, to the Queen's tenth. It was worth a princely sum—eighty thousand pounds.

" 'Tis more than ever a man presented Her Majesty as yet," Raleigh wrote later to Cecil. "If God has sent it as my ransom, I hope Her Majesty will accept it."

The Queen did accept it, and Raleigh and his wife were freed and went happily to their country home. But Elizabeth called Raleigh back to Court whenever she needed his help.

Never had England been so rich as it was now. Never had the English felt so safe. Nobles no longer built strong castles, with moats around them to protect themselves and their people. They built fine manors with big windows and many chimneys, and surrounded their houses with green lawns. Even the poor had pillows and mattresses to sleep on, where before they had had only bundles of reeds or straw.

The years of peace had given men time to think of other things than war and fighting. Poetry and plays were written and the great writings of other countries and other times were being translated into English.

Often the poets and playwrights met at the Mermaid Tavern. Whenever Raleigh came down to London he paid a visit to the tavern.

He knew that there he would find some of his friends. One afternoon when he walked into the tavern, Edmund Spenser, the great poet, greeted him.

"Edmund!" cried Raleigh affectionately. "How have you fared with Her Majesty?"

"It has been a long wait," replied Spenser, smiling. He looked weary and shabby. "But now at last I am commanded to read a part of my poem, 'The Faërie Queene,' at Court."

"Perhaps with Her Majesty's favor the play will some day be thought better entertainment than cock-fighting and bear-baiting," said Will Shakespeare. This young actor and playwright had come down to London two years before. "It seems a pity," he added, "that theatres must be built alongside the bear pit and the bull-bating ring."

"If you keep on drawing crowds to your plays as you do now, sweet Will," cried Christopher Marlowe, "a dozen new theatres will have to be built!"

"But you, Sir Walter," Spenser looked affectionately at his friend, "I hear that you are going to sail to the New World to search for gold in Guiana."

"Ah well," replied Raleigh, "gold lures settlers. The rich soil of Virginia did not draw many men there. Perhaps we can settle a colony in Guiana."

"What courage you have!" cried young Shakespeare. His beautiful eyes shone. "You must tell me of those strange and lovely tropic lands when you return, Sir Walter."

Raleigh did sail for Guiana in South America. He had a royal permit to "discover and conquer heathen lands." He found some gold up the Orinoco River. But the best thing he brought back was some medicine given him by an old Indian chief.

CHAPTER EIGHTEEN

The Gallant Queen

LONDON was very gay. The Thames was covered with pleasure boats. Only yesterday the Queen herself had come down the river on a barge decked in purple and gold, with sweet music playing.

Children rolled their hoops over the greens and sang merrily, "The Spanish ships came sailing by, from off the Spanish Main. The wind it rose, the storm it raged, and blew them half in twain."

Today Elizabeth wanted to look her best, for Master Shakespeare was coming to give his pretty play, "A Midsummer Night's Dream." Maybe there would be something about herself in it. She remembered how the poet Edmund Spenser had read a poem in her honor.

It was she herself, of course, who was "The Faërie Queene." She remembered the words:

". . . O Goddesse heavenly bright!
Mirrour of grace and Majestie divine,
Great Ladie of the greatest Isle, whose light
Like Phoebus lampe throughout the world doth shine . . ."

Yes, England was great. "My England," murmured the Queen. "I was wed to England. And to her have I ever kept faith."

Today she would wear the most splendid of her three thousand dresses. And the jewels which Raleigh had sent her. Her people liked her to look magnificent.

Her red wig was not curled right. She boxed

the ears of two serving women; then was sorry, and spoke sweetly to all.

When later she swept into the great hall of the palace Elizabeth looked magnificent. She stood in the doorway, in her gold and black brocade, sparkling with jewels. And with her flaming wig, she seemed young again.

The young noblemen pressed forward to meet her. They lifted their Queen from her feet, and carried her upon their shoulders all about the great hall, like a jeweled idol on a golden platform. Cheers and music burst forth as they lowered her gently to her throne.

That was a happy, splendid moment. But there were still troubles ahead for the Queen. In her court was a young man named Essex. He was her favorite courtier since Raleigh had married. But he was hotheaded and willful, often disobeying orders.

She had forgiven him many times. At last she learned that Essex was plotting against her and planning to overthrow the government. He was taken prisoner and tried. When he was found guilty, he was sentenced to death and beheaded.

The Queen had loved him and now she

grieved greatly. She seemed to age suddenly. There were times when, in her heavy robes, she could scarcely mount her throne. Yet she called Parliament to meet, to ask them to send money to people who were starving in Ireland.

Then she promised that no one person would be given the right to sell the wines, the wools, the cloths of England, and so make more money than he should. The Commons rose as one man to shout their thanks.

"I have more cause to thank you than you

have to thank me," the Queen replied. "For you have let me know about things which were harmful to the people." She spoke for a lengthy time.

Finally the lawmakers heard what were to be their Queen's last words to them.

"Though you may have many princes more mighty and wise sitting in this seat," she said, and her voice still rang strong, "yet you never had, or ever shall have, any that will be more careful and loving."

The year passed; weeks and months went by. The Queen was failing. She cared for nothing. Sir Walter Raleigh, ever the perfect gentleman and faithful knight, came once more to cheer and comfort her. He brought her the medicine which the old Guiana chief had given him.

It helped her for a time. The Queen seemed better. One day she even danced an Irish jig in a gay and sprightly way. The palace folk peeped from behind the curtains in astonishment.

But soon the Queen fell grievously ill. Her mind was sick as well as her body. She kept a sword at her side and sometimes she would suddenly thrust it through her bed curtains, as though some assassin hid there. The Queen, who had never been afraid!

She would not rest in bed, she would see no doctors. She ate and drank very little and she spoke not at all. She sat in her chair, or wandered about the corridors, stumbling and falling often. Her ladies ran before her as she walked, laying pillows for her thin body to fall upon.

And then one day, when she could not rise, she motioned her ladies to pull her to her feet.

"She stands, without moving!" her women cried softly, and they wept for the pity of it.

"Long ago a soothsayer said that Her Grace would die in bed," whispered Elspeth, who stood beside her. "And so Her Grace thinks that as long as she can keep out of bed, she will live."

For full fifteen hours the great Queen, the mighty Elizabeth, stood fighting off the dark shadow of the Angel of Death.

At last, she sank onto the cushions spread for her, and lay silent, her finger on her lips. Sir Robert Cecil begged to know whom she would name as her heir. But she would not answer. The Bishop prayed with her for long. Once more Cecil begged, "Shall James of Scotland be King?" At this she made a sign, though some said she spoke, saying, "Yes."

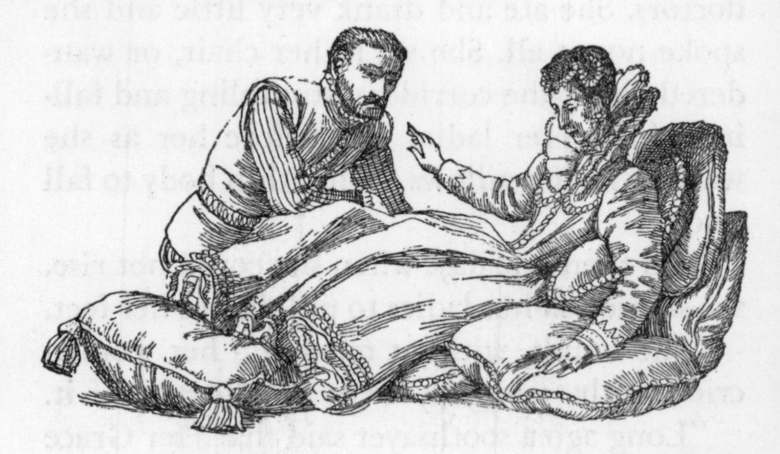

So quietly in the dawn of March the 24th, the year of 1603, she passed out of this life—Elizabeth, the Tudor Queen who had lived through such dangers and storms.

When she came to the throne England was divided, at war with itself, in debt. She left it strong, united, rich. Mistakes she made, wrongs she did, but . . .

"To England she has for fifty years given peace," said Sir Walter Raleigh, "when all the rest of the world was torn by wars. Her reign will forever be known as The Golden Age of Elizabeth."

"She drew great men around her," replied Sir Robert Cecil, "and gave them opportunity to do great deeds."

"Ay, more than that, Milords," said Giles, and there were tears in his eyes. "The lowliest soul in England loved our good Queen Bess as few rulers have been or ever shall be loved."

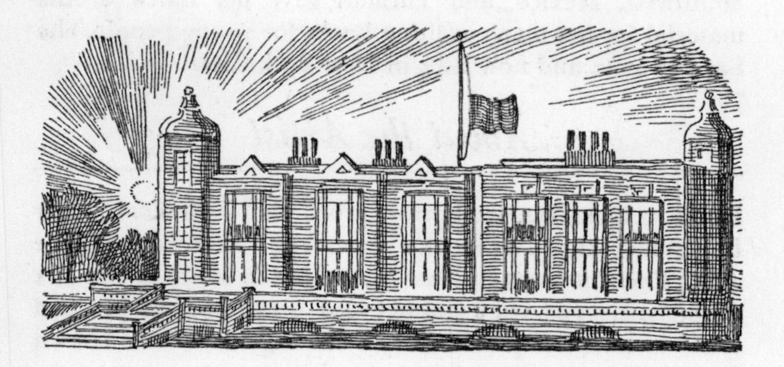

About the Author

ALIDA MALKUS was born in New York State, but she grew up in the Great Lakes country, in Bay City, Michigan. She learned to swim in Saginaw Bay, and since that time has swum in everything from a cattle tank on the western desert to the black waters of a sacred Maya well in Yucatan. At thirteen, she already had begun writing and drawing for the high school paper. Two years later, she went to art school in San Francisco. When she grew up, her adventures in the Southwest, Mexico, and Yucatan gave her much of the material for her many exciting books for young people. She has two sons, and now lives in New York City.

About the Artist

DOUGLAS GORSLINE was born in Rochester, New York. After he finished school, he spent a year at the Yale School of Fine Arts. Then he went to New York City to study at the Art Students League. As a painter and illustrator, he has had great success. His paintings and etchings have been shown in all the national exhibitions and have won many prizes. Now he is becoming known as a writer as well. He is the author of "What People Wore," a book about clothing worn through the ages in all countries of the world, and a book for boys and girls called "Farm Boy" which won a Herald Tribune Honor Citation for juveniles.

"Names That Made History"

ENID LAMONTE MEADOWCROFT, *Supervising Editor*

THE STORY OF GOOD QUEEN BESS
By Alida Sims Malkus. *Illustrated by Douglas Gorsline*

THE STORY OF BUFFALO BILL
By Edmund Collier. *Illustrated by Nicholas Eggenhofer*

THE STORY OF DANIEL BOONE
By William O. Steele. *Illustrated by Warren Baumgartner*

THE STORY OF KIT CARSON
By Edmund Collier. *Illustrated by Nicholas Eggenhofer*

THE STORY OF CHRISTOPHER COLUMBUS
By Nina Brown Baker. *Illustrated by David Hendrickson*

THE STORY OF DAVY CROCKETT
By Enid LaMonte Meadowcroft. *Illustrated by C. B. Falls*

THE STORY OF THOMAS ALVA EDISON
By Enid LaMonte Meadowcroft. *Illustrated by Harve Stein*

THE STORY OF BENJAMIN FRANKLIN
By Enid LaMonte Meadowcroft. *Illustrated by Edward A. Wilson*

THE STORY OF ULYSSES S. GRANT
By Jeannette Covert Nolan. *Illustrated by Lynd Ward*

THE STORY OF ANDREW JACKSON
By Enid LaMonte Meadowcroft. *Illustrated by David Hendrickson*

THE STORY OF JOAN OF ARC
By Jeannette Covert Nolan. *Illustrated by Pranas Lapé*

THE STORY OF JOHN PAUL JONES
By Iris Vinton. *Illustrated by Edward A. Wilson*

THE STORY OF LAFAYETTE
By Hazel Wilson. *Illustrated by Edy Legrand*

THE STORY OF ROBERT E. LEE
By Iris Vinton. *Illustrated by John Alan Maxwell*

THE STORY OF ABRAHAM LINCOLN
By Nina Brown Baker. *Illustrated by Warren Baumgartner*

THE STORY OF FLORENCE NIGHTINGALE
By Margaret Leighton. *Illustrated by Corinne B. Dillon*

THE STORY OF LOUIS PASTEUR
By Alida Sims Malkus. *Illustrated by Jo Spier*

THE STORY OF POCAHONTAS
By Shirley Graham. *Illustrated by Mario Cooper*

THE STORY OF MARCO POLO
By Olive Price. *Illustrated by Federico Castellon*

THE STORY OF THEODORE ROOSEVELT
By Winthrop Neilson. *Illustrated by Edward A. Wilson*

THE STORY OF MARK TWAIN
By Joan Howard. *Illustrated by Donald McKay*

THE STORY OF GEORGE WASHINGTON
By Enid LaMonte Meadowcroft. *Illustrated by Edward A. Wilson*

THE STORY OF MAD ANTHONY WAYNE
By Hazel Wilson. *Illustrated by Lawrence Beall Smith*

HANDSOME BOOKPLATES

If you would like a set of bookplates, so that you can write your own name in these books just the way the great signatures are shown, send your name and address to SIGNATURE BOOKS, GROSSET & DUNLAP, INC., 1107 Broadway, New York 10, N. Y. *We will mail you, upon receipt of ten cents to pay the cost of postage and handling, a set of handsomely designed bookplates, each one different.*

1 *Born at Greenwich, England,*
September 7, 1533

2 *Is recognized by Parliament as*
an heir to the throne, 1544

3 *Is imprisoned in the Tower by*
her sister, Mary Tudor, 1553

4 *Becomes Queen of England at Coronation*
in Westminster Abbey, 1559

10 *Dies at Richmond, England,*
March 24, 1603

9 *Names James of Scotland as her heir,*
uniting England and Scotland, 160